Applications
of
Graph Theory
to Group Structure

PRENTICE-HALL INTERNATIONAL, INC.   London
PRENTICE-HALL OF AUSTRALIA, PTY, LTD.   Sydney
PRENTICE-HALL OF CANADA, LTD.   Toronto
PRENTICE-HALL FRANCE, S.A.R.L.   Paris
PRENTICE-HALL OF JAPAN, INC.   Tokyo
PRENTICE-HALL DE MEXICO, S.A.   Mexico City

Prentice-Hall Series in Mathematical Analysis of Social Behavior

James Coleman and James March, *Editors*

Translated by

Maurice Pinard   McGill University and The Social Research Group

Raymond Breton   McGill University and The Social Research Group

Fernand Fontaine   University of Ottawa and The Social Research Group

Applications
of
Graph Theory
to Group Structure

Claude Flament

Department of Social Psychology
Laboratory of Social Sciences
Aix en Provence, France

PRENTICE-HALL, INC. ENGLEWOOD CLIFFS, NEW JERSEY

Current printing (last digit):
11 10 9 8 7 6 5 4 3

APPLICATIONS OF GRAPH THEORY
TO GROUP STRUCTURE
By Claude Flament
Translated by
Maurice Pinard
Raymond Breton
and Fernand Fontaine

Library of Congress Catalog Card Number 63-13845
Printed in the United States of America. (C)

Preface

It is easily granted that a science that has attained its maturity must become mathematical and must *therefore* make use of numbers.

This *therefore* seems to us to be contestable. Numbers — or more exactly numerical sets — are members of the family of mathematical structures. To translate a problem into mathematical terms consists of defining at least a partial isomorphism between this problem and an adequate mathematical structure. This structure may or may not be numerical, the essential aspect being that it is adequate: the isomorphism must be demonstrable.

The numerical structures are particularly rich — their properties are numerous and highly complex — but it is rare that a behavioral fact can be shown to have such properties (and even more rare that the question is raised); therefore a numerical model is rarely legitimate!

We shall therefore mathematize many problems of the behavioral sciences through the use of poorer structures, having fewer properties, and having properties that are simpler — that is, that can be more easily identified in reality.

The theory of graphs, which will be shown to be the mathematical theory of arbitrary relations, provides us with some of those structures that are poor in properties that cannot be observed in behavior, but that are rich in potentialities of application to the behavioral sciences.

It is often thought that the theory of graphs can be useful only for static descriptions; this is not the case, as we shall try to show in Chapter 3. But it must be admitted that all the potentialities of the theory of graphs as applied to the behavioral sciences have not yet been sufficiently explored to make it possible at the moment to give more than a few examples. This is the sole aim of this brief monograph.

I should like to extend my acknowledgement to those who, by their teaching in psychology and mathematics, by their encouragement and advice, helped me in my researches in mathematics as applied to the behavorial sciences: Professor P. Fraisse (Sorbonne), who directed all my research in communication networks; Professor G. Th. Guilbaut and Professor M. Barbut (Ecole Pratique des Hautes Etudes, Paris) and Professor J. M. Faverge (Université Libre de Bruxelles), who guided my mathematical training; my friend H. Rouanet (Centre d'Etudes et de Recherches Psychotechniques, Paris), whose fraternal and critical support has often been decisive; Claude Berge (Centre National de la Recherche Scientifique, Paris), whose book* as well as personal support have been the basis of the research here presented; Professor R. D. Luce, (Pennsylvania State University), whose works on the application of the theory of graphs to communication networks have been the starting point for my research; and Professor J.S.Coleman (The Johns Hopkins University), whose friendly insistence impelled me to write this book. Finally, I thank especially the translators who intelligently accomplished a considerable and thankless task.

CLAUDE FLAMENT

*Claude Berge, *Théorie des graphes et ses applications* (Paris: Dunod, 1958); English translation: *The Theory of Graphs and Its Applications* (London: Methuen; and New York: Wiley, 1962).

Contents

Applications
of
Graph Theory
to Group Structure

CHAPTER ONE

Introduction to the Theory of Graphs

1. Sets and Operations on Sets

1.1. Introduction

A *set* is a collection of objects of some sort; these objects are called *elements* or *points* of the set.

A set is usually denoted by a capital Latin letter, for instance: S, A, B, X, . . .; its elements are usually represented by small Latin letters: a, b, x, ... But this is only a general indication.

If a is an element of the set S, it is represented by

$$a \in S,$$

which is read: a belongs to S.

If a *is not* an element of S, it is represented by

$$a \notin S,$$

which is read: a does not belong to S.

If the elements of a set S are a, b, c, and d, it is represented by

$$S = \{a, b, c, d\}.$$

The order in which the elements of a set are written has no particular meaning:

$$\{a, b, c, d\} = \{b, d, c, a\}.$$

A set can be defined by the *list* of its elements, as above; it can also be

1

defined by a *property* that belongs to all its elements, such that all the elements having this property appear in the set; for instance, the set of prime numbers can be represented by

$$S = \{x \mid x \text{ is a prime number}\}.$$

This method allows one to think about a set the elements of which cannot, for one reason or another, be listed; one can thus deal with the property which characterizes the elements.

The *power* of a set is the number of its elements; it is denoted by the letter representing the set written between two vertical lines. The power of S is $|S|$.

The power of a set may be of any kind. We shall consider here only sets with *finite* powers. The theory of finite sets is extremely simple; difficulties appear only with infinite sets.

It is convenient to consider a set with a null power, that is, a set having no elements. It is called the *empty set* and is represented by $\emptyset$.

If a set S is constituted of only one element a, we write: $S = \{a\}$; a, which is an element, must be distinguished from $\{a\}$, which is a set.

It is often convenient to represent a set by a circle, called an *Euler circle*. The elements of the set are represented within the circle. Their concrete notation is often neglected: we *know* that the elements of a set are within the circle which represents the set. This technique will be shown below with regard to the operations on sets.

1.2. Union of Sets

Let $A = \{a, b, c\}$ and $B = \{c, d, e\}$ be two sets; the set C which is formed by the elements belonging to A or to B is called *union*, denoted

$$C = A \cup B = \{x \mid x \in A \text{ or } x \in B\}.$$

The *or* is not disjunctive: x may belong to A only, or to B only, or to both A *and B*. In the above illustration, we have

$$C = \{a, b, c, d, e\};$$

the element c belongs to both A and B.

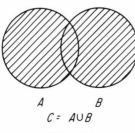

A B

$C = A \cup B$

Figure 1.1

In Fig. 1.1, the sets A and B are represented by Euler circles; the set C is not represented by a circle, but by the total hatched area.

The union of sets is often compared to the arithmetic sum. This analogy is dangerous. For instance, in general $|A| + |B| \neq |A \cup B|$; in the example above, we have $|A| = 3$, $|B| = 3$, and $|A \cup B| = 5$. On the other hand, the union is perfectly comparable with the *logical operation "or,"* which has in fact been utilized to define the union.

The union is *tautological* or *idempotent*: the union of a set with itself gives the set itself.

$$A \cup A = A.$$

It should be manifest that the operation of union follows the *commutative law*,

$$A \cup B = B \cup A,$$

as well as the *associative law*. Let A, B, and C be three sets; let $D = A \cup B$ and $E = C \cup D$. We can write

$$E = C \cup (A \cup B),$$

but it can also be written

$$E = (C \cup A) \cup B;$$

this is the associative law. We shall then write, without parentheses,

$$E = A \cup B \cup C.$$

Suppose we have r sets A_i $(i = 1, 2, \ldots, r)$; if we want to represent the union of these r sets, we can write, on the basis of the commutative and associative laws,

$$\bigcup_{i=1}^{r} A_i.$$

1.3. Intersection of Sets

The *intersection C* of two sets A and B is the set of elements which belongs *both* to A *and* B; we write

$$C = A \cap B = \{x \mid x \in a \text{ and } x \in B\}.$$

The hatched section of Fig. 1.2 represents the intersection.

If the sets have no common element, their intersection is *empty*: $A \cap B = \emptyset$. We then say that the sets are *disjoint*. Disjoint sets can be represented by non-secant Euler circles, but this is not necessary.

The intersection of sets is often compared to arithmetical multiplication. It is actually preferable to compare it to the *logical operation "and."*

The operation of intersection, like that of union, is tautological:

$$A \cap A = A;$$

and follows the commutative law:

$$A \cap B = B \cap A;$$

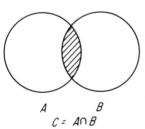

A B
$C = A \cap B$

Figure 1.2

and the associative law:

$$(A \cap B) \cap C = A \cap (B \cap C) = A \cap B \cap C.$$

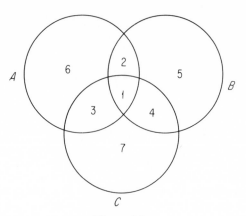

Figure 1.3

The intersection of several sets A_i $(i = 1, 2, \ldots, r)$, will be represented by

$$\bigcap_{i=1}^{r} A_i.$$

The operations of union and intersection both follow the *distributive law* with respect to one another, the union with respect to the intersection,

$$A \cup (B \cap C) = (A \cup B) \cap (A \cup C),$$

and the intersection with respect to the union,

$$A \cap (B \cup C) = (A \cap B) \cup (A \cap C).$$

These results (like the preceding ones) can be represented by Euler circles. Figure 1.3 shows three sets, A, B, and C. The *areas* of the figure have been numbered from 1 to 7; for instance, {1} refers to $A \cap B \cap C$. Consider the distributive law as applied to the union with respect to the intersection.

$$B \cap C = \{1, 4\}, \qquad A = \{1, 2, 3, 6,\}.$$

Hence $A \cup (B \cap C) = \{1, 2, 3, 6\} \cup \{1, 4\} = \{1, 2, 3, 4, 6\},$

$A \cup B = \{1, 2, 3, 4, 5, 6\}, \qquad A \cup C = \{1, 2, 3, 4, 6, 7\}.$

Hence $(A \cup B) \cap (A \cup C) = \{1, 2, 3, 4, 5, 6\} \cap \{1, 2, 3, 4, 6, 7\}$

$$= \{1, 2, 3, 4, 6\}.$$

Therefore $A \cup (B \cap C) = \{1, 2, 3, 4, 6\} = (A \cup B) \cap (A \cup C).$

Hence $A \cup (B \cap C) = (A \cup B) \cap (A \cup C).$

1.4. Difference and Symmetric Difference

The difference $C = A - B$ is the set of elements which belong to A and do not belong to B:

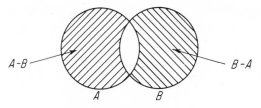

Figure 1.4

$$A - B = \{x \mid x \in A \text{ and } x \notin B\}.$$

We have $A - B \neq B - A$ (see Fig. 1.4).

The set of elements which belong to A and not to B and of elements which belong to B and not to A is called the *symmetric difference* of the two sets A and B. Symbolically,

$$C = A \oplus B;$$

this gives $\qquad A \oplus B = (A - B) \cup (B - A),$

but also $\qquad A \oplus B = (A \cup B) - (A \cap B) \qquad$ (see Fig. 1.4).

The symmetric difference is a commutative operation:

$$A \oplus B = B \oplus A.$$

1.5. Cartesian Product

Let $A = \{a, b, c, d\}$ and $B = \{x, y, z\}$, and construct an $\mid A \mid \times \mid B \mid$ table, with the elements of A as row headings and the elements of B as column headings. Within the cells, put the pairs consisting of the row-heading letter as a first term and the column-heading letter as a second term (the order in a pair is essential):

		$B =$		
		x	y	z
	a	(a, x)	(a, y)	(a, z)
	b	(b, x)	(b, y)	(b, z)
$A =$	c	(c, x)	(c, y)	(c, z)
	d	(d, x)	(d, y)	(d, z)

The set of pairs shown in the table is the Cartesian product C of the sets A and B (in this order):

$$C = AB = \{(a, x), (a, y), (a, z), \ldots, (d, z)\}.$$

The Cartesian product is an operation which is quite different from those presented above. The elements of the union, for instance, are of the same kind as the elements of each set, but here the elements of the product are of a new type: they are pairs of elements.

The Cartesian product, in general, does not follow the commutative law: $AB \neq BA$. This is due to the importance of the order of the terms in the pairs: $(a, x) \neq (x, a)$; but $(a, x) \in AB$, while $(x, a) \notin AB$; and $(x, a) \in BA$, while $(a, x) \notin BA$.

A special case of Cartesian product, which is very important as far as we are concerned, is the product of a set by itself, AA, which is represented by A^2, by analogy with arithmetical multiplication. If $A = \{a, b, c\}$, we have

$$A^2 = \{(a, a), (a, b), (a, c), (b, b), (b, c), (c, a), (c, b), (c, e)\}.$$

The pairs with two identical terms, $(a, a), (b, b), (c, c)$, are called *diagonal pairs*. Indeed, in the $|A| \times |A|$ table of the product, they are in the cells of one of the diagonals.

	a	b	c
a	(a, a)	(a, b)	(a, c)
b	(b, a)	(b, b)	(b, c)
c	(c, a)	(c, b)	(c, c)

1.6. Subsets; Inclusion

A set A' is a subset of the set A if all the elements of A' are elements of A (Fig. 1.5); we write $A' \subset A$, which is read: A' is included in A, or A' is a subset of A.

If $A' \subset A$, it is obvious (see the figure) that

$$A' \cap A = A',$$

and

$$A' \cup A = A.$$

It should be noted that the definition, "$A' \subset A$ implies that if $a \in A'$, then $a \in A$," does not say whether or not some elements of A do not belong to A'; in particular, $A \subset A$. If it is known that there exists at least one element of A which does not belong to A', it can be written as $A' \subset \subset A$, which is read: A' is *strictly* included in A.

The empty set is a subset of any set: $\emptyset \subset A$ for any set A.

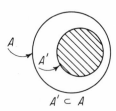

$A' \subset A$

Figure 1.5

1.7. Set of Parts; Partition

Given a set S, any subset S' of S is also called *part of S*; we may consider all the subsets of S, or all the parts of S. We call the *set of parts of S* the set of elements which are the subsets or parts of S—symbolically, $\mathfrak{p}(S)$; it is thus a *set of sets*.

If $S = \{a, b, c\}$, we have

$$\mathfrak{p}(S) = \{\emptyset, \{a\}, \{b\}, \{c\}, \{a, b\}, \{a, c\}, \{b, c\}, \{a, b, c\}\}.$$

Note that according to the definition of subsets, the empty set and the set S itself are part of $\mathfrak{p}(S)$.

Symbolically,

$$\mathfrak{p}(S) = \{S' \mid S' \subset S\}.$$

A *partition of S* consists of a subset of $\mathfrak{p}(S)$ which has some particular properties. Given r parts or subsets of S: $S'_1, S'_2, \ldots, S'_r$; this constitutes a partition of S if and only if

1. $\bigcup\limits_{i=1}^{r} S_i = S$;

2. for every i and every j, $1 \leq i, j \leq r$, if $i \neq j$, then

$$S'_i \cap S'_j = \emptyset.$$

In other words, the sets $S'_1, S'_2, \ldots, S'_r$ constitute a partition of S if and only if each element of S is present in one and only one S'_i.

If $S = \{a, b, c\}$, the sets $\{a\}$ and $\{b, c\}$ constitute a partition of S; $\{a\}$, $\{b\}$ and $\{c\}$ constitute another one; but $\{a\}$ and $\{a, b\}$ do *not* constitute a partition of S.

2. Relations and Functions

2.1. Introduction

Let S be a set and S^2 be the product of S by itself; let R be a subset of S^2:

$$R \subset S^2;$$

we say that *R is a relation defined over S*.

A relation is then a set of pairs. If a and $b \in S$, we have either $(a, b) \in R$, or $(a, b) \notin R$; if $(a, b) \in R$, the pair (a, b) is said to verify the relation R. Instead of $(a, b) \in R$, we often write

$$a \, R \, b.$$

It is in this form that the relations are usually handled. For instance,

R is an equality relation:

$$a = b;$$

R is a partial order:

$$a \geq b;$$

R is the orthogonal relation between the straight lines a and b:

$$a \perp b;$$

and so on.

Inclusion is a relation defined over the set of parts of a set. If $S = \{a, b, c\}$, the set $\mathrm{p}(S)$ of the parts of S will consist of $\{a\}$, $\{b\}$, $\{c\}$, $\{a, b\}$, etc. On $[\mathrm{p}(S)]^2$ we have an inclusion relation; for instance,

$$\{a\} \subset \{a, b\}.$$

A relation has been defined as a subset of the product of a set by itself; this is the most frequent case, but this is not the only one. Generally, if S and S' are two sets,

$$R \subset SS'$$

is a relation. If $S = S'$, we have the above case. But we can very well have $S \neq S'$.

For instance, the symbol $\in$, which indicates that an element belongs to a set, denotes a relation between the elements of a set S and the set $\mathrm{p}(S)$ of the parts of S.

A relation R defined over a set S: $R \subset S^2$, may have various properties, among others the following:

Reflexivity. All the pairs of the diagonal of S^2 belong to R: for every $a \in S$, $(a, a) \in R$, or $a \, R \, a$.

Symmetry. $(a, b) \in R \Leftrightarrow (b, a) \in R$.

Antisymmetry. If $(a, b) \in R$ and $(b, a) \in R$, then $a = b$.

Transitivity. $(a, b) \in R$ and $(b, c) \in R \Rightarrow (a, c) \in R$.

Some important types of relations are defined on the basis of these properties.

Weak ordering relation. The relation R is a weak ordering if it is reflexive and transitive. If a weak ordering is symmetrical, we have an equivalence relation; if it is antisymmetrical, we have an order relation.

2.2. Equivalence Relation

Examples. The equality relation is an equivalence relation; indeed, we have

$$a = a \qquad \text{(reflexivity)};$$

$$a = b \Leftrightarrow b = a \qquad \text{(symmetry)};$$

and $\qquad a = b \text{ and } b = c \Rightarrow a = c \qquad \text{(transitivity)}.$

The relation between straight lines, "to be parallel or coincident," is an equivalence relation, which is represented by $\|$. Indeed if $d, d',$ and d'' are straight lines, we have

$$d \parallel d$$

(reflexivity, since a straight line is coincident to itself);

$$d \parallel d' \Leftrightarrow d' \parallel d \qquad \text{(obvious symmetry)};$$

and $\qquad d \parallel d' \quad \text{and} \quad d' \parallel d'' \Rightarrow d \parallel d'' \qquad$ (transitivity).

The transitivity is not strictly obvious in this case; we know that two straight lines parallel to a third one are parallel, that is,

$$d \parallel d' \quad \text{and} \quad d'' \parallel d' \Rightarrow d \parallel d'',$$

which *is not* transitivity; but, if we use the symmetry, it is possible in this last expression to replace $d'' \parallel d'$ by $d' \parallel d''$, and we get the transitivity.

The similarity relation between individuals *is not* an equivalence relation. We may have reflexivity (Peter looks like himself) and symmetry (If Peter looks like Paul, then Paul looks like Peter), but there is no transitivity in general. Peter looks like Paul (because they have a face of a similar form); Paul looks like James (because they have similar eyes); but Peter and James have nothing in common and do not look like each other.

Equivalence classes. If R is an equivalent relation defined over a set S, we shall denote by $R(a) = \{x \mid x \in S, (a, x) \in R\}$ the set of elements of S which are equivalent to a. It should be noted that $a \in R(a)$, since $(a, a) \in R$ (reflexivity). By symmetry and transitivity of R, it can be shown that

$$x \in R(a) \quad \text{and} \quad y \in R(a) \Rightarrow (x, y) \in R.$$

Indeed, $\qquad x \in R(a) \Rightarrow (a, x) \in R \Rightarrow (x, a) \in R$

and $\qquad y \in R(a) \Rightarrow (a, y) \in R;$

but $\qquad (x, a) \in R \quad \text{and} \quad (a, y) \in R \Rightarrow (x, y) \in R.$

It follows that

$$(a, b) \in R \Rightarrow R(a) = R(b).$$

Such a set is called an *equivalence class.* As shown above, the definition of an equivalence class is independent of the element a from which we started. If we start from an element b equivalent to a, the same equivalence class is obtained.

If S is a set with an equivalence relation R, consider some element a of S; we obtain the equivalence class $C_1 = R(a)$. Consider now an element $b \notin C_1$ and let $C_2 = R(b)$; consider further an element $c \notin C_1 \cup C_2$ and let $C_3 = R(c)$; and in general, let

$$C_i = R(x) \qquad \text{with } x \notin \bigcup_{j=1}^{i-1} C_j.$$

Some of these classes may consist of a single element; the number of classes C_i is finite, since S is itself finite.

THEOREM 1.1. *The set of equivalence classes constitutes a partition of S.*

If indeed an element x of S does not belong to any equivalence class, it means that the process described is not completed, and we define a class

$C_j = R(x)$; then, once the process of construction is completed, we have

$$\bigcup_i C_i = S.$$

On the other hand, any two distinct classes C_i and C_j are disjoint: $C_i \cap C_j = \emptyset$. If indeed we had $x \in C_i \cap C_j$, this would imply

$$x \in C_i \Rightarrow R(x) = C_i$$

and

$$x \in C_j \Rightarrow R(x) = C_j.$$

Therefore $C_i = C_j$; the classes would be coincident.

2.3. Order Relation

Example. The relation of inclusion between the parts of a set is an order relation; indeed,

$$S \subset S$$

(reflexivity: any element of S is an element of S);

$$S \subset S' \quad \text{and} \quad S' \subset S'' \Rightarrow S \subset S''$$

(transitivity; see Fig. 1.6); and

$$S \subset S' \quad \text{and} \quad S' \subset S \Rightarrow S = S'$$

(antisymmetry: any element of S is an element of S' and any element of S' is an element of S; therefore S and S' possess the same elements).

But the relation of *strict* inclusion is not an order relation: it is not reflexive.

It can be seen, on the basis of the property of antisymmetry, that an order relation R over a set S *induces* an equivalence relation R^* over this same set:

$$(a, b) \in R^* \quad \text{if and only if} \quad (a, b) \in R \quad \text{and} \quad (b, a) \in R.$$

Let C be the set of equivalence classes defined by R^* over S,

$$C = \{C_1, C_2, \ldots\},$$

define a relation R' between the elements of C, that is, between the equivalence classes: $(C_i, C_j) \in R'$, if and only if we can find $a \in C_i$ and $b \in C_j$ such that $(a, b) \in R$.

THEOREM 1.2. *If $(C_i, C_j) \in R'$, for every $x \in C_i$ and every $y \in C_j$, we get $(x, y) \in R$.*

Indeed,

$$x \in C_i \quad \text{and} \quad a \in C_i \Rightarrow (x, a) \in R^* \Rightarrow (x, a) \in R;$$

$$y \in C_j \quad \text{and} \quad b \in C_j \Rightarrow (b, y) \in R^* \Rightarrow (b, y) \in R;$$

but we have $(a, b) \in R$; hence

$$(x, a) \in R \quad \text{and} \quad (a, b) \in R \Rightarrow (x, b) \in R,$$

and $(x, b) \in R \quad \text{and} \quad (b, y) \in R \Rightarrow (x, y) \in R.$

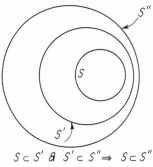

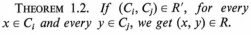
$S \subset S' \, \& \, S' \subset S'' \Rightarrow S \subset S''$

Figure 1.6

THEOREM 1.3. *R' is an order relation over the equivalence classes.*

Indeed, if $a \in C_i$, $b \in C_j$, and $c \in C_k$, then

$$(a, a) \in R \quad \text{and} \quad (C_i, C_i) \in R' \qquad \text{(reflexivity)};$$

$$[(C_i, C_j) \in R' \text{ and } (C_j, C_i) \in R'] \Rightarrow [(a, b) \in R \text{ and } (b, a) \in R]$$

$$\Rightarrow [(a, b) \in R^*]$$

$$\Rightarrow [C_i = C_j] \qquad \text{(antisymmetry)}:$$

$$[(C_i, C_j) \in R' \text{ and } (C_j, C_k) \in R'] \Rightarrow [(a, b) \in R \text{ and } (b, c) \in R]$$

$$\Rightarrow [(a, c) \in R]$$

$$\Rightarrow [(C_i, C_k) \in R'] \qquad \text{(transitivity)}.$$

2.4. Function

A function mapping a set A into a set B is a relation defined over the product $A \, \mathfrak{p}(B)$ and such that for each element a of A, there is an element B' of $\mathfrak{p}(B)$, and only one, which verifies the relation. In fact, a function can be reduced to a relation R between A and B. Define (as done previously with regard to equivalence classes) for every $a \in A$:

$$R(a) = \{b \mid b \in B, \ (a, b) \in R\}.$$

$R(a)$ is evidently a part of B, that is, an element of $\mathfrak{p}(B)$. The function is established between each element a of A and the elements $R(a)$ of $\mathfrak{p}(B)$.

A function is usually written as a Greek capital letter: Γ, Δ, Φ, ...

The part of B which corresponds to a through the function Γ is called the *image* of $a \in A$, and is represented symbolically by Γa. If a relation R is associated to Γ, as above, we get $\Gamma a = R(a)$.

We may indeed speak of a function or of a relation indifferently, without any risk of error.

If A' is a part of A, and Γ a function mapping A into B, we define

$$\Gamma A' = \bigcup_{a \in A'} \Gamma a$$

The function Γ^-, inverse of Γ, is a function mapping B into A defined by

$$\Gamma^- b = \{a \mid a \in A, \ b \in \Gamma a\}.$$

As well as a relation, a function Γ may be defined over a single set S: if $x \in S$, $\Gamma x \in \mathfrak{p}(S)$.

We may then consider:

$$\Gamma^2 x = \Gamma(\Gamma x) = \bigcup_{y \in \Gamma x} \Gamma y;$$

$$\Gamma^3 x = \Gamma(\Gamma^2 x);$$

$$\Gamma^k x = \Gamma(\Gamma^{k-1} x).$$

If we have two functions, Γ and Δ, defined over the same set S, we get the products

$$\Gamma\Delta x = \Gamma(\Delta x) = \bigcup_{y\in\Delta x} \Gamma y;$$

and

$$\Delta\Gamma x = \Delta(\Gamma x) = \bigcup_{y\in\Gamma x} \Delta y;$$

generally:

$$\Gamma\Delta \neq \Delta\Gamma.$$

2.5. Table of a Function or of a Relation

Consider the table of the Cartesian product of two sets A and B (where $B \neq A$ or $B = A$). We know that for each cell there is a pair (a, b), with $a \in A$ and $b \in B$; there is no use in including this pair in the corresponding cell. Since a relation R is a subset of a product AB, it can be represented by writing, for instance, a plus sign $(+)$ in the cells corresponding to the pairs which verify the relation R. If, for instance, $A = \{a, b, c\}$, $B = \{x, y, z\}$, and $R = \{(a, y), (a, z), (b, x), (b, z)\}$, the following table is obtained:

	$B =$		
	x	y	z
a		$+$	$+$
$A = b$	$+$		$+$
c			

One can immediately read in this table:

$$R(a) = \{y, z\}; \qquad R(b) = \{x, z\}; \qquad R(c) = \emptyset.$$

This table may just as well be considered as representing a mapping of A into B; and one reads, for instance,

$$\Gamma a = \{y, z\}, \qquad \Gamma b = \{x, z\},$$
$$\Gamma\{a, b\} = \{x, y, z\}, \quad \Gamma^- z = \{a, b\}, \quad \text{etc.}$$

3. Ordered Sets; Lattices

3.1. Ordered Sets

Let S be a set with an order relation R; S is then called an ordered set. If a and $b \in S$ and $(a, b) \in R$, we write

$$a \geqq b,$$

which is read: a is greater than or equal to b. This need not mean that a is a number greater than b; it may mean that person a takes precedence over person b, or that word a in a text precedes word b, etc.

Two elements a and b of S are *comparable* if either $a \geq b$ or $b \geq a$ or both; otherwise they are incomparable. If all the elements of S taken two at a time are comparable, S is *completely ordered*.

If we have $a \geq b$ but *not* $b \geq a$, it can be written $a > b$, which is read: a is *strictly* greater than b ($>$ is not, properly speaking, an order relation, since there is no reflexivity; we speak of a *strict order*).

If $a > b$ and if there is no element c in S such that $a > c$ and $c > b$, we say that a *covers* b.

If in S there is no element strictly greater than $a \in S$, a is a *maximal* element of S; if in S there is no element strictly smaller than $b \in S$, b is a *minimal* element of S.

3.2. Representation of an Ordered Set

It is often convenient to represent graphically an ordered set. In order to do so, we consider all the minimal elements of S and we represent them by (geometric) points horizontally arranged *at the bottom* of the drawing; then, horizontally and immediately above them, we lay out the elements in such a way that all other elements which they cover are already represented at a lower level; and we go on like this till the end.

After that, we draw a line between two elements if and only if one of them covers the other.

Consider a set $S = \{a, b, c, d, e, f\}$ with an order relation whose table is as follows:

	a	b	c	d	e	f
a	+		+			
b		+				
c			+			
d		+		+		
e		+			+	
f		+	+	+	+	+

This gives the representation of Fig. 1.7.

Note that f is greater than b; but f does not cover b; there is therefore no line between b and f in the figure. However, the fact ($f > b$) can be deduced

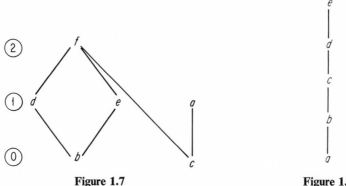

Figure 1.7   Figure 1.8

in the drawing from the lines (*fd*) and (*db*) [or (*fe*) and (*eb*)] which express
$f > d$ and $d > b$, hence $f > b$, by virtue of transitivity.

The lowest horizontal layout in the drawing is the zero *level*; the next one,
the level 1; etc.; the levels are indicated in Fig. 1.7.

It can easily be verified that if S is *completely* ordered, there is but one element at each level, as in Fig. 1.8; the drawing then looks like a *chain*, or a line.
This is why a completely ordered set is also called *linearly* ordered.

3.3. Lattices

Let S be an ordered set. An element a of S is the *superior limit* for $S' \subset S$
if all elements of S' are less than or equal to a, and if there does not exist $a' \in S$
less than a and having this property. The *inferior limit* of S' is defined in an
analogous way.

A finite ordered set is a *lattice* if and only if everyone of its parts possesses a
superior limit and an inferior limit.

Figure 1.7 does *not* present a lattice, while Fig. 1.8 does.

We shall be concerned here only with ordered sets of a very particular kind:
the set of parts of a set, ordered by the relation of inclusion.

Let $S = \{a, b, c\}$ be a set; we have

$$\mathfrak{p}(S) = \{\emptyset, \{a\}, \{b\}, \{c\}, \{a, b\}, \{a, c\}, \{b, c\}, \{a, b, c\} \}.$$

The set $\mathfrak{p}(S)$ is a *lattice*: the superior limit of a subset of parts is their union;
their inferior limit is their intersection.

Figure 1.9 gives a representation of the lattice $\mathfrak{p}(S)$.

Certain properties of a lattice $\mathfrak{p}(S)$ should be noted. If S' covers S'' and
S''' we get $S' = S'' \cup S'''$; for instance, $\{b, c\}$ covers $\{b\}$ and $\{c\}$. If S' is
covered by both S'' and S''', we get $S' = S'' \cap S'''$; for instance, $\{c\}$ is
covered by $\{a, c\}$ and $\{b, c\}$.

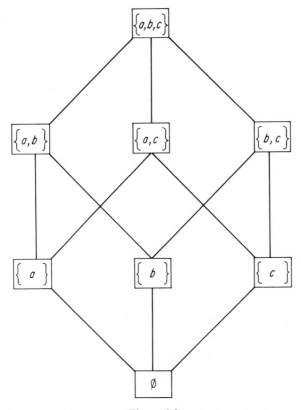

Figure 1.9

4. Distances in a Set

We define a *distance* over a set S if to each pair (a, b) of S a number $d(a, b)$ with the following properties can be associated:

1. $d(a, b) \geq 0$, and $d(a, b) = 0$ if and only if $a = b$;
2. $d(a, b) = d(b, a)$;
3. $d(a, b) + d(b, c) \geq d(a, c)$.

The mathematical notion of distance does not always coincide with the common notion. For instance, one may speak of the distance covered in going from one place to another in a city; because of one-way streets, however, the routes from a to b and from b to a may be different and may not have the same length; the second property is not met.

On the other hand it is not intuitive that the power of the symmetric difference of two sets is a distance; mathematically, however, it is a distance, and this notion is very useful in the social sciences (see, for instance, Restle, 1959 and 1961). Let us consider this type of distance.

Given the sets S_i $(i = 1, 2, \ldots, r)$, put

$$d(S_i, S_j) = |\, S_i \oplus S_j \,|;$$

$d(S_i, S_j)$ is the number of elements of S_i which do not belong to S_j, plus the number of elements of S_j which do not belong to S_i.

Since $d(S_i, S_j)$ is the power of a set, this is a positive number or zero if the set is empty; if the set is empty, all the elements of S_i belong to S_j, and all the elements of S_j belong to S_i, that is $S_i = S_j$. The first property is met.

The symmetric difference is a commutative operation; therefore

$$(S_i \oplus S_j) = (S_j \oplus S_i),$$

hence

$$d(S_i, S_j) = |\, S_i \oplus S_j \,| = |\, S_j \oplus S_i \,| = d(S_j, S_i).$$

The second property is met.

In order that the third property be met, let us make use of the Eulerian circles which represent the relations between three sets S_i, S_j, and S_k (Fig. 1.10).

We have

$$S_i \oplus S_j = \{3, 4, 5, 6\},$$
$$S_i \oplus S_k = \{2, 3, 5, 7\},$$

and

$$S_j \oplus S_k = \{2, 4, 6, 7\};$$

hence

$$d(S_i, S_j) = |\, 3 \,| + |\, 4 \,| + |\, 5 \,| + |\, 6 \,|,$$
$$d(S_i, S_k) = |\, 2 \,| + |\, 3 \,| + |\, 5 \,| + |\, 7 \,|,$$

and

$$d(S_j, S_k) = |\, 2 \,| + |\, 4 \,| + |\, 6 \,| + |\, 7 \,|.$$

This gives

$$d(S_i, S_j) + d(S_j, S_k) = |\, 2 \,| + |\, 3 \,| + 2|\, 4 \,| + |\, 5 \,| + 2|\, 6 \,| + |\, 7 \,|,$$

and

$$d(S_i, S_j) + d(S_j, S_k) - d(S_i, S_k) = 2(|\, 4 \,| + |\, 6 \,|) \geqq 0,$$

hence

$$d(S_i, S_j) + d(S_j, S_k) \geqq d(S_i, S_k).$$

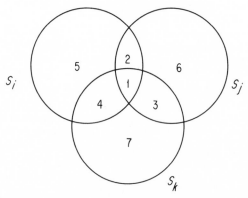

Figure 1.10

THEOREM 1.4

$$d(S_i, S_j) = d[S_i, (S_i \cup S_j)] + d[(S_i \cup S_j), S_j]$$
$$= d[S_i, (S_i \cap S_j)] + d[(S_i \cap S_j), S_j].$$

Proof. It was shown in the definition of the symmetric difference of two sets A and B that $A \oplus B = (A-B) \cup (B-A)$. Therefore

$$S_i \oplus (S_i \cup S_j) = [S_i - (S_i \cup S_j)] \cup [S_i \cup S_j) - S_j];$$

but
$$S_i - (S_i \cup S_j) = \emptyset$$

and
$$(S_i \cup S_j) - S_j = S_i - S_j;$$

hence
$$S_i \oplus (S_i \cup S_j) = S_i - S_j;$$

similarly,
$$(S_i \cup S_j) + S_j = S_j - S_i.$$

The sets $(S_i - S_j)$ and $(S_j - S_i)$ being evidently disjoint, the power of their union is the sum of their powers:

$$|(S_i - S_j) \cup (S_j - S_i)| = |S_i - S_j| + |S_j - S_i|;$$

but
$$(S_i - S_j) \cup (S_j - S_i) = S_i \oplus S_j;$$

hence
$$|S_i \oplus S_j| = |S_i - S_j| + |S_j - S_i|$$
$$= |S_i \oplus (S_i \cup S_j)| + |(S_i \cup S_j) \oplus S_j|$$

and
$$d(S_i, S_j) = d[S_i, (S_i \cup S_j)] + d[(S_i \cup S_j), S_j].$$

We show in the same way the second equality of the theorem. These demonstrations can be visualized in the Eulerian circles appearing in Fig. 1.10.

THEOREM 1.5. *If S_i and S_j are two parts of S, the distance $d(S_i, S_j)$ is equal to the number of lines which constitute the shortest path from S_i to S_j in the graphic representation of the lattice* $p(S)$.

Proof. In a lattice $p(S)$, an element S' covers an element S'' if and only if $S'' \subset S'$ and $|S' - S''| = 1$ (see Fig. 1.11); therefore, to the line of the drawing of $p(S)$ we can associate an element of S: to the line $(S'S'')$ we associate the element which constitutes $(S' \oplus S'')$ (Fig. 1.11). It can easily be shown that n lines start from each point of $p(S)$ if S has n elements ($|S| = n$), each element of S being associated with one of these lines.

Now consider the elements of $(S_i \oplus S_j)$, in any order: $x_1, x_2, \ldots$. For example, if $S_i = \{a\}$ and $S_j = \{b, c\}$, we have b, c, a. We leave S_i by the line associated with the first element of $(S_i \oplus S_j)$; we reach the element $S_i \cup \{x_1\}$ if $x_1 \in (S_j - S_i)$ or $S_i - \{x_1\}$ if $x_1 \in (S_i - S_j)$; then from this element we use the line associated with x_2; etc. We thus reach S_j by a number of steps equal to $|S_i \oplus S_j|$, that is, $d(S_i, S_j)$. This path is in fact the shortest (or one of the shortest); indeed, to a shorter path would correspond a set of elements of S which would not comprise at least one x_i of $(S_i \oplus S_j)$, and this element x_i would not be removed from S_i, though it should be, or would not be united to S_i, though it should be: S_j would not be reached.

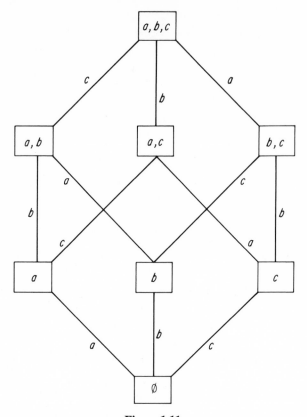

Figure 1.11

In the example $S_i = \{a\}$ and $S_j = \{b, c\}$, one can follow the path b, c, a: $\{a\}$, $\{a, b\}$, $\{a, b, c\}$, $\{b, c\}$, or the path a, b, c: $\{a\}$, $\emptyset$, $\{b\}$, $\{b, c\}$, etc. (Fig. 1.11).

5. Graphs and Paths of a Graph

5.1. Introduction

If we have a set X and a function Γ over this set, we have a *graph G*, which can be denoted

$$G = (X; \Gamma).$$

We sometimes consider the set V of the pairs of X^2 such as x and $y \in X$ and $y \in \Gamma x$; we then write $G = (X; V)$. Since we easily proceed from Γ to V and from V to Γ, the two notations are equivalent.

Any element of V is an *arc* of the graph.

The elements of X are the *points* of the graph.

The correspondence Γ may have remarkable properties, which define particular graphs.

Symmetric graph: for any x and $y \in X$, we have

$$(x, y) \in V \Leftrightarrow (y, x) \in V.$$

Transitive graph:

$$(x, y) \in V \quad \text{and} \quad (y, z) \in V \Rightarrow (x, z) \in V.$$

Complete graph: for any x and $y \in X$, we have

$$\text{either} \quad (x, y) \in V \quad \text{or} \quad (y, x) \in V \quad \text{or both.}$$

Reflexive graph: for any $x \in X$, we have

$$(x, x) \in V;$$

such an arc (x, x) is called a *loop*.

These terms and notations are already familiar: a symmetric graph corresponds to a symmetric relation; a complete transitive graph, to a complete order relation; etc. Indeed, the theory of graphs and the theory of relations are somewhat similar. But these two theories are more or less useful depending on the applications; the theory of relations is more useful, perhaps, for the study of particular relations (equivalence, order); the theory of graphs is without doubt more useful for the study of *arbitrary relations*.

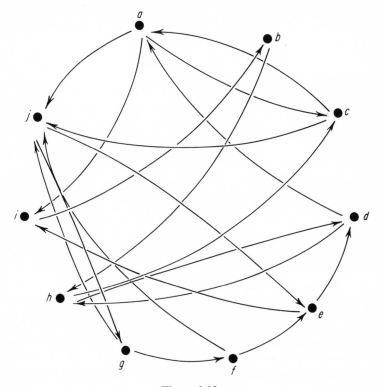

Figure 1.12

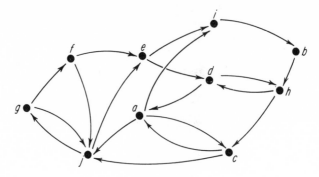

Figure 1.13

5.2. Representation of a Graph

Let $G = (X, \Gamma) = (X, V)$ be a graph; it can be represented by a drawing in the following way. The elements of X are represented by (geometric) points *arranged in a completely arbitrary way* in the drawing; we draw an *arrow* from x to y if and only if $(x, y) \in V$. Figures 1.12 and 1.13 present examples. The graphs represented there are actually identical; the arrangement of points is the only difference and it has no particular meaning. However, a "good" arrangement makes the reading of the drawing easier; this is merely a matter of convenience, without any theoretical relevance.

5.3. The Matrix Associated with a Graph

We have seen how to associate a table with a relation; here the principle is exactly the same. If G has $n = |X|$ points, we form a matrix (or table) with n rows and n columns. To the ith row we associate the point $x_i \in X$; to the jth column, the point $x_j \in X$. Within the cells, the elements of the matrix are denoted by g_{ij}; put $g_{ij} = 1$ if $(x_i, x_j) \in V$, and $g_{ij} = 0$ if $(x_i, x_j) \in V$.

If G denotes a graph, we shall refer to its associated matrix by $\|G\|$. The matrix associated with the graph of Fig. 1.13 is as shown on page 21. (Zeros are frequently omitted from such a matrix for typographic reasons.)

It will be seen that the matrix associated with a graph makes the study of some properties of the graph easier. It can already be used to set forth the following definitions:

The *degree of emission,* or the *external semi-degree,* of a point $x_i \in X$ is

$$d^+(x_i) = \sum_{j=1}^{n} g_{ij};$$

this is the number of arcs *leading out* of x_i; e.g., $d^+(a) = 3$.

The *degree of reception,* or the *internal semi-degree,* of a point $x_j \in X$ is

$$d^-(x_j) = \sum_{i=1}^{n} g_{ij};$$

this is the number of arcs incident into x_j; e.g., $d^-(a) = 2$.

	a	b	c	d	e	f	g	h	i	j
a			1						1	1
b								1		
c	1									1
d	1						1			
e				1				1		
f					1					1
g						1				1
h			1	1						
i		1								
j					1		1			

Application. A sociometric test is administered in a social group; each member of the group chooses a certain number (possibly none) of his peers. We call X the set of the members of the group (each individual is an element of X), and we put $(x, y) \in V$ if and only if x chose y. $G = (X, V)$ is the *sociogram*; $\| G \|$, the sociomatrix; $d^+(x)$ measures the sociometric expansibility of x; $d^-(x)$, the popularity or sociometric status of x. (Note that a sociogram is a graph without loops, since a member cannot choose himself.)

5.4. Subgraph, Partial Graph, and Reduced Graph

Subgraph. Let $G = (X; \Gamma) = (X; V)$ be a graph. $G' = (X'; \Gamma) = (X'; V')$ is a *subgraph* of G if

$$X' \subset X$$

and if

$$x \in X': \quad \Gamma X' = \Gamma x \cap X';$$

or, if one prefers, $(x, y) \in V'$ if and only if $(x, y) \in V$, and x and $y \in X'$. Stated otherwise, certain points and the arcs leading out of or incident into these points are deleted from X. The matrix $\| G' \|$ is obtained by removing from the matric $\| G \|$ the rows and columns corresponding to the points of $X - X'$. The graph of Fig. 1.14 is a subgraph of the graph of Fig. 1.13. Its associated matrix is as follows:

	a	b	c	d
a			1	
b				
c	1			
d	1			

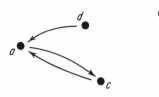

Partial graph. $G' = (X'; V')$ is a *partial graph* of $G = (X; V)$ if

$$X' = X \quad \text{and} \quad V' \subset \subset V.$$

All the points of G are kept and some of its arcs are deleted. $\| G' \|$ is obtained by making zero some of the nonzero cells of $\| G \|$. The graph of Fig. 1.15 is a partial graph of Fig. 1.13.

Figure 1.14

Bringing the notions of a subgraph and of a partial graph together, the notion of a *partial subgraph* can be obtained: subgraph of a partial graph, or partial graph of a subgraph. The graph of Fig. 1.16 is a partial subgraph of the graph of Fig. 1-13.

Reduction of a graph. Let $G = (X; \Gamma)$ be a graph; define over X a partition $X_1, X_2, \ldots, X_r$, with

$$\bigcup_{i=1}^{r} X_i = X \quad \text{and} \quad X_i \cap X_j = \emptyset$$

for every $i, j = 1, 2, \ldots, r$. Let $X^0 = \{X_1, X_2, \ldots, X_r\}$ be the set of parts thus defined, and let Γ^0 over X^0 be a function defined by: $(X_i, X_j) \in \Gamma^0$ if and only if there exist a point $x \in X_i$ and a point $y \in X_j$ such that $(x, y) \in \Gamma$. The graph $G^0 = (X^0, \Gamma^0)$ is a *reduced graph* of the graph G. Figure 1.17 presents a graph G and a reduced graph G^0 of G.

Obviously, many reduced graphs can be obtained from a graph. The interest in such an operation is contingent upon the properties of the partition of the points of the graph. Specifically, the reduction of a graph obtained on the basis of a partition which results from an equivalence relation over the points of the graph can reveal unknown phenomena.

Example. A graph represents a given type of relation among the members of a firm; the set of points are partitioned on the basis of whether or not they belong to the various departments of the firm.

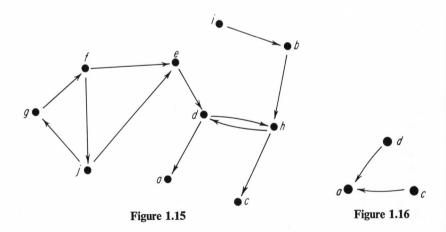

Figure 1.15   Figure 1.16

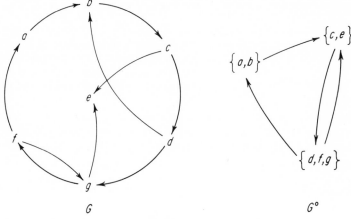

Figure 1.17

5.5. Paths of a Graph

We call a *path* of a graph $G = (X; V)$ a completely ordered subset V' of V such that the kth arc of V' ends at the point of X from which the $(k + 1)$th arc is coming out; if x is the source of the first arc of V' and y, the ending of the last arc of V', the path may be denoted $\gamma(xy)$.

Example. In the graph of Fig. 1.15, let $V' = \{(j, e), (e, d), (d, a)\}$; we get a path $\gamma(ja)$. If one wants to specify that this path goes through d, one denotes it by $\gamma(j. . .da)$. If one wants to specify all the steps of the path, one writes $\gamma(jeda)$.

If the graph represents a road network with its one-way streets, we realize that a path represents in fact a possible route.

A path is *elementary* if it never goes twice through the same point. In Fig. 1.15, $\gamma(jeda)$ is an elementary path, but $\gamma(jedhda)$ is not.

A *circuit* is a path which comes back to its point of departure. In Fig. 1.15, $\gamma(dhd)$ and $\gamma(gfjg)$ are circuits. One can obviously follow a circuit from any arbitrary point in it:

$$\gamma(gfjg) = \gamma(fjgf) = \gamma(jgfj).$$

Chains and cycles. It is sometimes necessary to consider a graph without paying attention to the direction of the arrows. For instance, one decides to follow an arc indifferently either in the direction of the arrow or in the opposite direction. This amounts to a transformation of the graph into a symmetric graph.

In such a case, the term *arc* is replaced by *edge*, the term *path*, by *chain*, the term *circuit*, by *cycle*.

In the graph of Fig. 1.15, for instance, we do not get the arc (e, j), but the edge (e, j). The series of arcs (d, h), (b, h), (i, b) does not constitute a path, but the corresponding edges (d, h), (h, b), and (b, i) constitute a chain. The arcs (f, e), (f, j) and (j, e) do not constitute a circuit, but the edges (f, e), (e, j) and (j, f) constitute a cycle.

In a nonsymmetric graph, there need not be a path wherever there is a chain; but in a symmetric graph, to a chain there always correspond two paths which are in opposite directions. (We get the same relations between a circuit and a cycle.)

Hamiltonian paths and circuits. A *Hamiltonian path* is an elementary path which goes through all the points of the graph. A *Hamiltonian circuit* is a Hamiltonian path which comes back to its point of departure.

In the graph of Fig. 1.13, the circuit (*acjgeibhda*) is a Hamiltonian circuit.

Hamiltonian paths and circuits create annoying problems for the theory of graphs (Camion, 1960; Flament, 1959a; Harary and Ross, 1954).

5.6. Arborescences and Trees

A graph $G = (X; V)$ is an *arborescence* with *root a* if

1. every point $x \in X$, where $x \neq a$, has a degree of reception equal to one;
2. the degree of reception of a is zero;
3. G does not contain any circuit.

An arborescence always looks like the graph in Fig. 1.18.

An arborescence is a set of divergent paths; we speak of the points with a degree of emission greater than one as *branching*.

If $G = (X; V)$ is an arborescence, the number of arcs of G is $|V| = (n-1)$, if the number of points of G is $|X| = n$. Indeed, this is deduced from the definition according to which all the points, except one (the root), receive one and only one arc.

The notion of a *tree* corresponds to that of an arborescence when the direction of the arcs is overlooked, or, if one prefers, when a symmetric graph is considered.

A tree is a set of edges (as opposed to arcs) which constitutes a graph

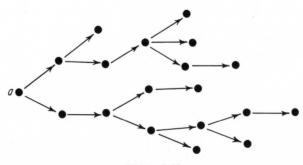

Figure 1.18

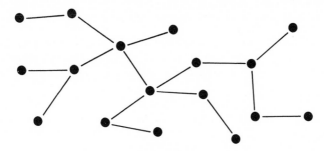

Figure 1.19

with $(n - 1)$ edges (as opposed to arcs) and without cycles (as opposed to circuits).

It is obvious that an arborescence constitutes a tree, while in general the converse is not true. A tree has no root, or rather, every point of a tree may be considered as a root—that is, as a point of departure to follow successively all the chains of the tree.

Figure 1.19 represents a tree.

6. Lengths and Deviations in a Graph

6.1. Introduction

The length of a path γ, denoted $l(\gamma)$, is measured, by definition, by the number of arcs which constitute the path.

From a point x to a point y, there may be many paths $\gamma_i(xy)$; the *deviation from x to y* is, by definition,

$$e(xy) = \min_i \{l[\gamma_i(xy)]\}.$$

This is the length of the shortest path from x to y.

A path $\gamma(xy)$ whose length is equal to $e(xy)$ is a *track*, which is denoted $\theta(xy)$.

The deviation is not generally a distance.

Indeed, when the graph is not symmetric, to go from y to x we are often compelled to pass through points different from those by which we pass to go from x to y; and there is no need for the tracks $\theta(xy)$ and $\theta(yx)$ to be of the same length. For instance, in the graph of Fig. 1.20, we have

$$e(ab) = 1,$$

that is, the length of the track $\theta(ab)$ consisting exclusively of the arc (a, b); and

$$e(ba) = 2,$$

that is, the length of the track $\theta(ba)$ consisting of the arcs (b, c) and (c, a). In order to have $e(ba) = 1$, the arc (b, a) should exist in the graph, which is not the case.

But in a symmetric graph, the deviations are distances.
If there is no path from x to y, conventionally we write

$$e(xy) = \infty \text{ (infinity)}.$$

The deviation from a point to itself is generally considered equal to zero: $e(xx) = 0$. This convention, which is quite normal, is moreover necessary in order for the deviation to become a distance in a symmetric graph.

6.2. Finding the Deviations

There exist many algorithmic methods to compute the deviation from one point to another. Rigorous methods have to be used in order to avoid the errors which are always made by the simple visual inspection of a graph, when it is somewhat complex. Of course, these methods are not necessary when the graph is as simple as the one presented in Fig. 1.20, where the paths, the tracks, and the deviations can immediately be seen.

We shall present first a method of graphic *marking*, and second, a matrix method (using the matrix associated with the graph).

The marking method to compute the deviations from one point to all others. In a graph $G = (X; \Gamma)$, to obtain the deviations from the point $a \in X$ to all the points of X, we proceed according to the following steps:

1. We mark as 0 (zero) the point a.
2. We mark as k the points not already marked and which are part of $(\Gamma^k x)$.
3. We stop when there are no more points, either because all the points of X are already marked or because the points which are not marked cannot be reached from the marked ones.
4. If $y \in X$ is marked k, this means that $e(xy) = k$; if $y \in X$ is not marked, this means that $e(xy) = \infty$.

Example. Consider the graph in Fig. 1.20.

The marking can be presented in the following way:

$$k = 0 \quad 1 \quad 2$$

$$\rightarrow b \rightarrow c$$
$$a$$
$$\rightarrow d$$

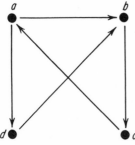

Figure 1.20

We should mark after d, in column 2, the point b, since (d, b) is an arc of the graph; but b is already marked. After c, there is only a left, which is already marked; then the process is completed. We get

$$e(ab) = e(ad) = 1; \qquad e(ac) = 2.$$

If we want the deviations from d to other points, we have

$$k = 0 \quad 1 \quad 2 \quad 3$$
$$d \rightarrow b \rightarrow c \rightarrow a$$

Deviation matrix. If we consider the deviations from all the points of X, the computed figures can be entered into the deviation matrix, which is designated by $E(G)$ if G represents the graph. In the cell (x, y) we enter the deviation $e(x, y)$. In the case of the graph in Fig. 1.20, we get

	a	b	c	d
a	0	1	2	1
b	2	0	1	3
c	1	2	0	2
d	3	1	2	0

Before we discuss the matrix method mentioned above, we might do well to review some basic principles of matrix theory.

Matrix theory. Let M be a matrix with n rows and p columns; it has order $(n \times p)$; the element of the cell (ij) is m_{ij}.

Addition. In order to be able to add a matrix M and a matrix Q, they must be of the same order; then we get

$$M + Q = R,$$

whose elements are

$$r_{ij} = m_{ij} + q_{ij}.$$

Example.

M					Q					R			
1	0	3	2		−2	4	1	3		−1	4	4	5
0	2	1	1	+	−3	−1	0	−1	=	−3	1	1	0
4	−1	2	0		2	1	0	2		6	0	2	2

Multiplication. In order to be able to multiply two matrices, the number of columns of one of them must be equal to the number of rows of the other. It is possible to multiply M by Q: MQ, if the order of M is $(n \times p)$ and the order of Q, $(p \times t)$. But we cannot then multiply Q by M: QM.

The order of M being $(n \times p)$ and the order of Q being $(p \times t)$, we have

$$R = MQ$$

with
$$r_{ij} = \sum_{k=1}^{p} m_{ik} \cdot q_{kj};$$

the order of R is $(n \times t)$.

Example.

M

1	−2
3	0
2	1

Q

2	−1	−3	0
1	2	0	1

$R = MQ =$

0	−5	−3	−2
6	−3	−9	0
5	0	−6	1

In order to obtain the number 6 of the second row, first column, of R, we take the second row of M: 3; 0; and the first column of Q: 2; 1; and then we multiply term by term:

$$
\begin{array}{cc}
3 & 0 \\
2 & 1 \\
\hline
6 & 0
\end{array}
$$

Hence
$$6 + 0 = 6.$$

Powers of a square matrix. If M is a matrix whose order is $(n \times n)$, or square matrix, it can be multiplied by itself to obtain its second power:

$$M^2 = MM$$

Similarly we define $M^r = M(M^{r-1}) = (M^{r-1})M$. The elements of M^r are denoted by $m_{ij}^{(r)}$.

If we repeatedly apply the multiplication formula, we get

$$m_{ij}^{(r)} = \sum_{k_1=1}^{n} \cdot \sum_{k_2=1}^{n} \cdots \sum_{k_{r-1}=1}^{n} m_{ik_1} \cdot m_{k_1 k_2} \cdots m_{k_{r-1}j}.$$

Example.

$M =$

0	1	0	1
0	0	1	0
1	0	0	0
0	1	0	0

;

$M^2 =$

0	1	1	0
1	0	0	0
0	1	0	1
0	0	1	0

;

$$M^3 = \begin{array}{|c|c|c|c|} \hline 1 & 0 & 1 & 0 \\ \hline 0 & 1 & 0 & 1 \\ \hline 0 & 1 & 1 & 0 \\ \hline 1 & 0 & 0 & 0 \\ \hline \end{array} \quad ; \quad \text{and so on.}$$

The matrix method for the computation of deviations.

THEOREM 1.6. (Festinger, 1949). *In a graph G, the number of paths, whether elementary or not, from x_i to x_j, whose length is r, is given by the element $g_{ij}^{(r)}$ of the rth power of the matrix $\| G \|$ associated with G.*

Proof. If a path $\gamma(x_i x_j)$ of length r exists in G, it is of the form

$$(x_i x_{k_1}), \quad (x_{k_1} x_{k_2}), \quad \ldots, \quad (x_{k_{r-1}} x_j);$$

we then have in $\| G \|$:

$$g_{ik_1} = g_{k_1 k_2} = \cdots = g_{k_{r-1} j} = 1,$$

and the product of these terms is equal to one. But this product,

$$g_{ik_1} \cdot g_{k_1 k_2} \cdots \cdot g_{k_{r-1} j},$$

is one of the terms of $g_{ij}^{(r)}$. Therefore, every path $\gamma(x_i x_j)$ of length r contributes a value equal to one to $g_{ij}^{(r)}$. Conversely, if a term of $g_{ij}^{(r)}$ is equal to one, this means that it corresponds to a path; indeed, if $g_{ik_1} \cdot g_{k_1 k_2} \cdots \cdot g_{k_{r-1} j} = 0$, this implies that at least one $g_{kk'}$ is equal to 0, which means that the arc $(x_k x_{k'})$ is lacking for the corresponding path.

THEOREM 1.7. *In a graph G with n points, the length of an elementary path is at the most equal to $(n - 1)$.*

Proof. If a path is made of m arcs, it obviously has $(m + 1)$ points, counting the initial point and the terminal point. Since an elementary path does not go twice through a same point, the longest elementary path in G that one can imagine is a path which goes through all the points of X, once and only once. Hence this path is of length $(n - 1)$.

From these theorems follows a simple algorithm for the computation of the deviations in graph G:

1. Compute the successive powers of $\| G \|$, at the most up to the power $r = n - 1$ if G has n points.
2. The deviation $e(xy)$ is equal to the smallest power r of $\| G \|$ where the cell (xy) comprises a term $g_{xy}^{(r)}$ *not equal to zero.*
3. If for any $r \leq n - 1$, $g_{xy}^{(r)} = 0$, we have $e(xy) = \infty$.
4. For all x, we put $e(xx) = 0$.

The example used previously for the computation of the powers of a matrix corresponds to the study of the graph of Fig. 1.20. We can deduce from it the following deviation matrix:

	a	b	c	d
a	0	1	2	1
b	2	0	1	3
c	1	2	0	2
d	3	1	2	0

We obviously get the same results as those found with the marking method. The advantage of the matrix method is that it can easily be programmed for a computer (see Ross and Harary, 1955).

6.3. Finding the Tracks between Two Points

Recall that a track $\theta(xy)$ is a path $\gamma(xy)$ of length equal to the deviation $e(xy)$.

THEOREM 1.8. *The point z is located on a track $\theta(xy)$ if and only if*

$$e(xz) + e(zy) = e(xy).$$

Proof. Sufficient condition. If $e(xz) + e(zy) = e(xy)$, consider the path $\gamma(xy)$ consisting of a track $\theta(xz)$ and a track $\theta(zy)$; the length of this path is $e(xy)$; hence it is a track $\theta(xy)$.

Necessary condition. A theorem by Bratton (1955) (see Berge, 1958, chap. 13, theorem 5) states that if $\theta(x...x_i...x_j...y)$ is a track, the path $\gamma(x_i...x_j)$ is a track; if z is a point of a track $\theta(xy)$, the segments (xz) and (zy) of this track are tracks $\theta(xz)$ and $\theta(zy)$, and their length is $e(xz)$ and $e(zy)$. Hence $e(xz) + e(zy)$ is the length of $\theta(xy)$.

THEOREM 1.9. *If z and z' both belong to a track $\theta(xy)$, the arc (zz'), if it exists, belongs to a track $\theta(xy)$ if and only if $e(xz) + 1 = e(xz')$.*

Proof. Sufficient condition. Consider the path consisting of a track $\theta(xz)$, the arc (zz'), and a track $\theta(z'y)$. The length of this path $\gamma(xy)$ is

$$l[\gamma(xy)] = e(xz) + 1 + e(z'y).$$

If $e(xz') = e(xz) + 1$, we get

$$l[\gamma(xy)] = e(xz') + e(z'y).$$

Since z' is on a track $\theta(xy)$, according to Theorem 1.8, we have

$$l[\gamma(xy)] = e(xy),$$

and this path is a track $\theta(xy)$.

Necessary condition. Suppose that the arc (zz') belongs to a track $\theta(xy)$. According to Bratton's theorem, the segments (xz) and (xz') of $\theta(xy)$ are of length $e(xz)$ and $e(xz')$; the segment (xz') consists of the segment (xz) and the arc (zz'); hence its length is $e(xz') = e(xz) + 1$.

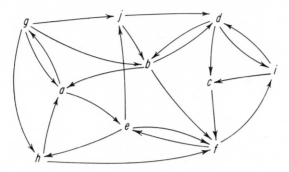

Figure 1.21

THEOREM 1.10 *Let* $\Theta(xy) = (X'; V')$ *be a partial subgraph of* $G = (X; V)$ *constructed in the following way*:

$X' \subset X$ *and* $V' \subset V$;

$z \in X' \Leftrightarrow e(xz) + e(zy) = e(xy)$;

$(z, z') \in V' \Leftrightarrow z$ *and* $z' \in X'$ *and* $e(xz) + 1 = e(xz')$.

All the paths $\gamma(xy)$ *in* $\Theta(xy)$ *are tracks* $\theta(xy)$ *in* G, *and all the tracks* $\theta(xy)$ *of G appear in* $\Theta(xy)$.

This theorem follows directly from the two previous ones. It provides an algorithm permitting us to find the tracks $\theta(xy)$ in a graph G.

Example. Consider the graph G of Fig. 1.21.

We want to construct $\Theta(ac)$. By one of the methods presented above, we compute the deviations $e(ax)$ and $e(xc)$ for every point x of G. We find

x	a	b	c	d	e	f	g	h	i	j
$e(ax)$	0	2	4	3	1	2	1	2	3	2
$e(xc)$	4	2	0	1	3	2	3	3	1	2
$e(ax)+e(xc)$	4	4	4	4	4	4	4	5	4	4

All the points of G, except h, belong to $\Theta(ac)$. Place these points x from

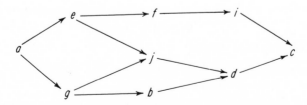

Figure 1.22

$$c \longrightarrow f \longrightarrow e \longrightarrow h \longrightarrow a$$

Figure 1.23

left to right, according to $e(ax)$, and draw the arcs (xy) which exist in G if y is to the right of x. We obtain Fig. 1.22, which represents $\Theta(ac)$.

Hence we get four tracks $\theta(ac)$:

$$aefic, \quad agjdc, \quad agjdc, \quad agbdc$$

Figure 1.23 presents $\Theta(ca)$, which has nothing in common with $\Theta(ac)$.

Finding other types of paths. Various studies offer methods to find paths of a given type, the knowledge of which may be useful: elementary paths (Ross and Harary, 1952); Hamiltonian paths and circuits (Camion, 1960; Flament, 1959; Harary and Ross, 1954); circuits and paths of a given length (Roy, 1961).

7. Connectivity of a Graph and Kindred Notions

7.1. Introduction

The notion of *connectivity* is important for the application of the theory of graphs to the social sciences: it is a mathematical translation of at least one aspect of the psychological notion of *group cohesiveness*. Intuitively it refers to the density of relationships.

The definitions to be presented are the results of the work of Roy (1961), Harary (1959c) and Luce (1950, 1952b).

7.2. Types of Connectivity

Let $G = (X; \Gamma)$ be a graph. G is *strongly connected* if for every pair (x, y) of points in G, there exists at least one path $\gamma(xy)$ in G. The graph of Fig. 1.24 is strongly connected since from any point we can go to any other one.

G is *semi-strongly connected* or *unilaterally connected* if, for any pair of points x, y in G, there exists a path $\gamma(xy)$ or a path $\gamma(yx)$ in G (Fig. 1.25).

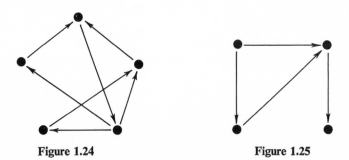

Figure 1.24   **Figure 1.25**

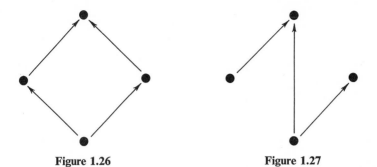

Figure 1.26   **Figure 1.27**

G is *quasi-strongly connected* if, for any pair of points *x*, *y* in *G*, there exist in *G* a point *z* and a point *z'* (eventually equal to *x* or *y*) such that some paths $\gamma(xz)$, $\gamma(yz)$, $\gamma(z'x)$ and $\gamma(z'y)$ are present in *G* (Fig. 1.26).

G is *simply connected* or *weakly connected* if for any pair (*x*, *y*) of *G*, there exists a chain (*xy*) in *G* (Fig. 1.27).

THEOREM 1.11. *A strongly connected graph is semi-strongly connected. A semi-strongly connected graph is quasi-strongly connected. A quasi-strongly connected graph is weakly connected.*

Proof. Strong connectivity entails semi-strong connectivity: this is self-evident. Semi-strong connectivity entails quasi-strong connectivity: if the path $\gamma(xy)$ exists, it is sufficient to put $x = z'$ and $y = z$. Quasi-strong connectivity entails weak connectivity: we have, for instance, the chain (*xy*) consisting of the paths $\gamma(xz)$ and $\gamma(yz)$.

This theorem actually establishes an *order* of the types of connectivity. From the highest to the lowest connectivity, we have: strong connectivity, semi-strong connectivity, quasi-strong connectivity, weak connectivity.

A weakly connected graph is a *connected graph*.

A graph which is not at least weakly connected is *unconnected*. A graph which is not connected is such that we can divide its points into at least two parts, the latter being such that there is no arc (*x*, *y*), with *x* in one part and *y* in another (Fig. 1.28).

Notice that a *symmetric* connected graph is always strongly connected.

We give the name *maximal connected component of a given type* of a graph *G* to any subgraph of *G* which

1. is connected of the given type;

2. is not a subgraph of a connected subgraph of the given type of *G*.

Example. In the graph of Fig. 1.29, which is only weakly connected, the subgraph defined by {*a*, *b*} is strongly connected, but does not constitute a maximal strongly connected component, since the subgraph defined by {*a*, *b*, *c*} is strongly connected. The latter subgraph is a maximal strongly connected component; but this subgraph is not a maximal semi-strongly con-

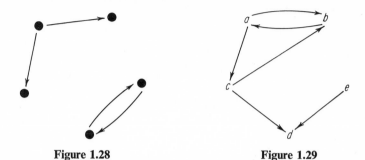

Figure 1.28   Figure 1.29

nected component, since the subgraph defined by $\{a, b, c, d\}$ is semi-strongly connected.

THEOREM 1.12. *The relations R and R' defined over the set X of the points of a graph G by*

$(x, y) \in R \Leftrightarrow x$ and y belong to the same maximal strongly
        connected component of G;

$(x, y) \in R' \Leftrightarrow x$ and y belong to the same maximal weakly
        connected component of G;

are equivalence relations.

Proof. $(x, y) \in R$ means: there exist in G a path $\gamma(x, y)$ and a path $\gamma(y, x)$.
R is reflexive: we get the path $\gamma(x, x)$, which consists of the paths $\gamma(x, y)$ and $\gamma(y, x)$ joined end to end.
R is obviously symmetric.
R is transitive: if $(x, y) \in R$ and $(y, z) \in R$, it implies that the paths $\gamma(x, y)$ and $\gamma(y, z)$, which give the path $\gamma(x. . .y. . .z)$, and the paths $\gamma(zy)$ and $\gamma(yx)$, which give the path $\gamma(z. . .y. . .x)$, exist; hence $(x, z) \in R$.
In the case of R' we replace path by chain in the argument.
(By convention, a subgraph made of only one point is considered a strongly connected one.)
Hence the points of a maximal strongly (or weakly) connected component constitute an equivalence class.

It should be noted that $(x, y) \in R \Rightarrow (x, y) \in R'$ (see Theorem 1.11). The converse, however, is not generally true.

THEOREM 1.13. *A graph $G = (X; \Gamma)$ is strongly connected if and only if, a being a given point of X, it is possible to go from a to all the points of X and from all the points of X to a.*

Proof. Let a be any arbitrary point of X. For any $x \in X$, we have paths $\gamma(ax)$ and $\gamma(xa)$; hence $(ax) \in R$. Therefore X constitutes a unique equivalence class for R, and G is strongly connected.

Finding the maximal strongly connected components of a graph by marking (Roy's algorithm, 1961).

1. Choose a point a in the graph; mark it with the signs ($\pm$).
2. If a point x of the graph is marked ($+$), mark with ($+$) all points of Γx.
3. If a point x is marked ($-$), mark with ($-$) all the points of $\Gamma^{-}x$.
4. When we cannot mark any more points, those which are marked ($\pm$) constitute a maximal strongly connected component containing a.
5. Start all over again with one of the points which does not belong to this component.

Example. In the graph presented in Fig. 1.29, we mark the point a with ($\pm$); then we mark with ($+$) the points b and c, then the point d. We mark with ($-$) the point b, then the point c. The maximal strongly connected component containing a is defined by $\{a, b, c\}$ (Fig. 1.30). We then find that d and e each constitute alone a maximal strongly connected component.

Remark. If a graph G has a certain type of connectivity, this entails certain properties for the deviation matrix $E(G)$.

If there is no infinite deviation (∞) in $E(G)$, G is strongly connected.

If in $E(G)$ any infinite deviation in a cell (xy) is accompanied by a noninfinite deviation in the symmetric cell (yx), G is semi-strongly connected.

The graph of Fig. 1.31 is semi-strongly connected, and is not strongly connected. Its deviation matrix is as follows:

	a	b	c	d	e
a	0	1	1	2	2
b	1	0	1	2	2
c	2	3	0	1	1
d	∞	∞	∞	0	∞
e	1	2	2	1	0

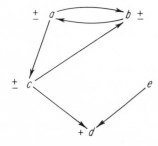

Figure 1.30

Figure 1.31

The subgraph defined by the removal of the point d is strongly connected, since its deviation matrix is as follows:

	a	b	c	e
a	0	1	1	2
b	1	0	1	2
c	2	3	0	1
e	1	2	2	0

7.3. Degree of Connectivity

Within the same type of connectivity, the graphs can be distinguished further. For instance, the two graphs of Fig. 1.32 are strongly connected, but it is sufficient to delete only one arc in α to change the type of connectivity, while in β it is necessary to delete two.

Luce (1950) calls *degree of connectivity* of a graph the minimal number of arcs that must be deleted in order to make it unconnected. This definition originated within the framework of the study of symmetric graphs, which comprise only one type of connectivity. In the general framework, we can consider the minimal number of arcs which must be deleted in order for the graph to change from its original type of connectivity to a lower one.

We then call the *degree of connectivity relative to a given type of connectivity* the minimal number of arcs which must be deleted to change to the given type of connectivity.

The problems related to the degrees of connectivity have been investigated fairly little, except for the case of the degree relative to the nonconnectivity, considered by Luce. We shall consider below some kindred notions which were introduced by Roy (1961) (see Chap. 2, Sec. 4.2, the notions of deletable arcs within the framework of the μ-equivalence).

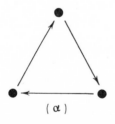

(α)

Figure 1.32α

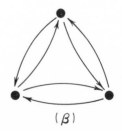

(β)

Figure 1.32β

7.4. Cliques

$G' = (X'; V')$, a subgraph of $G = (X; V)$, is a clique if $(x, y) \in V' \Leftrightarrow x$ and $y \in X'$, that is, if all the possible arcs exist in G'. This is a systematization of a current notion in *sociometry*: all the individuals of a clique choose each other.

A maximal clique is a clique which is not a subgraph of a clique.

A complete symmetric graph amounts to a maximal unique clique (see Fig. 1.32β).

Harary and Ross (1957) present a matrix method to find maximal cliques in a graph. Another method, based on Boolean algebra, is used in France though it has not yet appeared in print.

Luce (1950) introduces the notions of a *generalized clique*, or clique of order m:

$G' = (X'; V')$, a subgraph of $G = (X; V)$, is a clique of order m if for every pair (x, y) of points in X', we have in G

$$e(xy) \leqq m.$$

A clique of order $m = 1$ is a clique in the proper sense of the word.

Let $G^{(m)} = (X; V^{(m)})$ be a graph constructed from $G = (X; V)$ by putting $(x, y) \in V^{(m)}$ if and only if $e(xy) \leqq m$. It is obvious that the cliques (of order 1) of $G^{(m)}$ are the cliques of order m of G. The methods used to find the cliques can therefore be applied.

7.5. Stability and Kernel of a Graph

Let $G = (X; V) = (X; \Gamma)$ be a graph. A set $S \subset X$ is *internally stable* if x and $y \in S \Rightarrow (x, y) \notin V$, or, if one prefers, if $\Gamma S \cap S = \emptyset$.

In the graph of Fig. 1.33, the set $S = \{e, f, g, h\}$ is internally stable; this is not the only internally stable set of this graph.

Let $G = (X; V)$ be a graph; construct a graph $\bar{G} = (X; \bar{V})$ by putting for every pair (x, y), x and $y \in X$, $x \neq y$,

$$(x, y) \in \bar{V} \Leftrightarrow (x, y) \notin V.$$

It is obvious that an internally stable set of G defines a clique in $\bar{G}$.

A set $T \subset X$ is externally stable if for every $x \in X$, $x \notin T$, we have

$$(\Gamma x) \cap T \neq \emptyset.$$

The set $\{e, f, g, h\}$ of the graph of Fig. 1.33 is externally stable, since from every point external to this set there is an arc which leads out and ends at a point of this set.

In some games with two teams, each member of a team has to watch a member of the other team. If X_1 and X_2 are the members of the two teams, respectively, put $G = (X; V)$ with $X = X_1 \cup X_2$ and with $(x, y) \in V$ if x is watched by y. It is then necessary for X_1 and X_2 to be externally stable sets.

A *kernel* is a set $N \subset X$ which is *both* internally and externally stable. The set $\{e, f, g, h\}$ in the graph of Fig. 1.33 is a kernel.

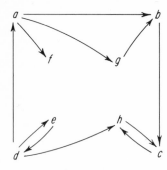

Consider a tournament consisting of two matches A and B; each participant in the tournament has a given strength in each match. Let X be the set of practice points and $G = (X; V)$, where $(x, y) \in V$ if and only if x is weaker than y for *both* matches. The tournament will actually be fought only between the members of the kernel of G (Figs. 1.34 and 1.35).

Frey (1960) has shown the advantages of these notions for the study of power structures in social groups.

Berge (1958, Chaps. 4 and 5) has investigated the numerous properties of stable sets and of kernels.

Figure 1.33

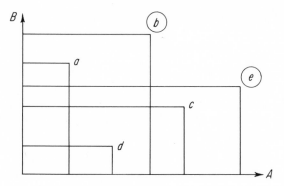

Figure 1.34

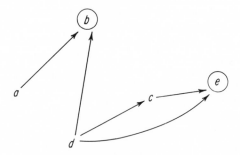

Figure 1.35

7.6. Articulation Point and Set. Power of a Point

A point a of a graph $G = (X; \Gamma)$ is an *articulation point* of G if the subgraph of $G: G' = (X'; \Gamma')$, defined by $X' = X - \{a\}$, is an unconnected graph. In Fig. 1.36, the point a is an articulation point.

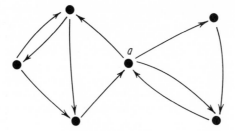

Figure 1.36

Generally the individual who is an articulation point in a graph thus occupies a privileged position. Since he ensures the connection between many subgroups, the relationships—whether good or bad—between these subgroups are dependent on him.

Ross and Harary (1955) have presented a method to find the articulation points in a graph.

The notion of articulation point has been generalized in two directions.

In a graph $G = (X; \Gamma)$, a set $A \subset X$ in an articulation set of G if the subgraph of $G: G' = (X'; \Gamma')$, defined by $X' = X - A$, is an unconnected graph. In Fig. 1.37, $\{a, b\}$ is an articulation set. Obviously, an articulation point is an articulation set reduced to a single point.

In a group, the points of an articulation set have the privileged position of an articulation point only if they make a *coalition*.

We have seen that an articulation point in a graph G is a point whose removal from G makes the graph of a certain type of connectivity an unconnected one. Ross and Harary (1959) suggest considering each point of a graph to see what its removal entails for the graph's type of connectivity: the removal of certain points may lower its connectivity, while the removal of others may raise it. These are weakening or strengthening points. Hence the notion of the *power of a point*. An articulation point is obviously a weakening point. The graph in Fig. 1.38 is strongly connected, but the removal of any point in this graph produces a graph which is no longer strongly connected. Therefore all these points are weakening points; they are not, however, articulation points. The graph in Fig. 1.39 is not strongly connected, but the removal of the point a produces a strongly connected graph; therefore this point is a strengthening point.

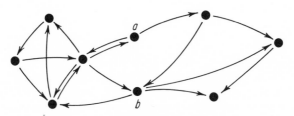

Figure 1.37

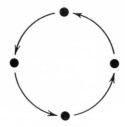

Figure 1.38

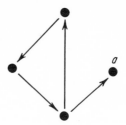

Figure 1.39

8. The Set of *n*-Points Graphs

8.1. Introduction

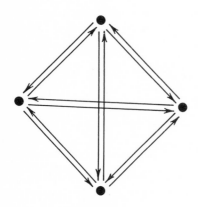

Figure 1.40

Let $G^{(n)} = (X; V^{(n)})$ be the completed symmetric graph without loop constructed over $|X| = n$ points. This graph is unique. We have $|V^{(n)}| = n(n-1)$ arcs (since here we limit ourselves to graphs without loop). $G^{(4)}$ is represented in Fig. 1.40.

All the *n*-points graphs constructed over the set X are partial graphs of $G^{(n)}$. Let $\mathscr{G}_n$ be the set of these graphs. There exist in this set of graphs some noticeable relations; we shall now consider some of them (some others will be considered later, such as the μ-equivalence relation of Roy; see Chap. 2, Sec. 4.2).

8.2. Isomorphism

Let $G_1 = (X; V_1)$ and $G_2 = (X; V_2)$ be two graphs. Since they are both constructed over the same set X, they are both part of the same set $\mathscr{G}_n$ (with $n = |X|$).

G_1 and G_2 are isomorphic if a biunique function f can be established between the points of $X = \{x_1, x_2, \ldots, x_n\}$,

$$f(x_i) = x_j,$$

the function being such that for any pair of points in X we have

$$(x_i, x_j) \in V_1 \Leftrightarrow (f(x_i), f(x_j)) \in V_2.$$

Stated otherwise, we simply have to replace each point $x_i \in X$ by the point $f(x_i)$ to go from G_1 to G_2, without affecting the arcs of the graph.

The two graphs in Figs. 1.41 and 1.42 are different, but they are isomorphic,

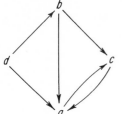
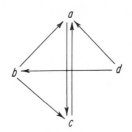
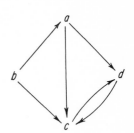

| Figure 1.41 | Figure 1.42 | Figure 1.43 |

with the function establishing the correspondence between their points as follows:

$$f(a) = b, \qquad f(c) = a,$$
$$f(b) = d, \qquad f(d) = c.$$

The isomorphism is more easily observed if we compare to the graph of Fig. 1.41 the graph of Fig. 1.43, which is identical to that of Fig. 1.42, but whose disposition permits us to visualize the function f ($f(x)$ has the same geometric disposition as x).

The relation of isomorphism, $(G_i, G_j) \in I$ if and only if G_i and G_j are isomorphic, is an equivalence relation in $\mathscr{G}_n$. Indeed, $(G_i, G_i) \in I$ (*reflexivity*), f being the identity function: $f(x) = x$ for any $x \in X$;

$$(G_i, G_j) \in I \Leftrightarrow (G_j, G_i) \in I \quad (symmetry),$$

the function being then f^{-1}. Since f is biunique, we have $f^{-1}f(x) = x$; and finally

$$(G_i, G_j) \in I \quad \text{and} \quad (G_j, G_k) \in I \Rightarrow (G_i, G_k) \in I \quad (transitivity).$$

If f_1 is the function mapping G_i into G_j and f_2 is the function mapping G_j into G_k, the function $f = f_2 f_1$ maps G_i into G_k, and

$$(x_h, x_e) \in V_i \Rightarrow [f_1(x_h), f_1(x_e)] \in V_j$$
$$\Rightarrow [f_2(f_1(x_h)), f_2(f_1(x_e))] \in V_k;$$

hence $\qquad (x_h, x_e) \in V_i \Rightarrow [f(x_h), f(x_e)] \in V_k.$

8.3. Lattices of n-Points Graphs

Consider the set $V^{(n)}$ of the arcs of the complete symmetric graph of n-points $G^{(n)}$. We know how to construct the set $p(V^{(n)})$ from the parts of $V^{(n)}$ (see Sec. 1.7) and the lattice of $p(V^{(n)})$ (see Sec. 3.3). For instance, if $n = 3$ and $X = \{a, b, c\}$, we have

$$V^{(3)} = \{(a, b), (b, a), (a, c), (c, a), (b, c), (c, b)\};$$

$V^{(3)}$ has six elements, and $p(V^{(3)})$ has $2^6 = 64$ elements; the lattice of $p(V^{(3)})$ is difficult to represent.

Let the graph $G_i = (X; V_i)$ correspond to each part V_i of $V^{(n)}$; we then construct all the n-points graphs. The set $\mathscr{G}_n$ therefore corresponds to $p(V^{(n)})$.

Since $p(V^{(n)})$ is ordered by inclusion, we can define an order relation over $\mathscr{G}_n$, which will also be called inclusion:

$$V_i \subset V_j \Rightarrow G_i = (X; V_i) \subset G_j = (X; V_j).$$

If $G_i \subset G_j$, we shall say that G_i is included in G_j, or else that G_i is a partial graph of G_j (Sec. 5.4).

The set $\mathscr{G}_n$ ordered by inclusion constitutes a lattice $\mathscr{L}_n$, in the same way as $p(V^{(n)})$.

8.4. σ-Equivalence—Lattices of n-Points Symmetric Graphs

Let $G_i = (X; V_i)$ be a graph. Construct a graph $G_i^\sigma = (X; V_i^\sigma)$, where V_i^σ is defined by $(x, y) \in V_i^\sigma$ if $(x, y) \in V_i$, or $(y, x) \in V_i$, or both. We move from G_i to G_i^σ by symmetrically arranging G_i.

We shall say that the two graphs G_i and G_j are σ-equivalent if and only if $G_i^\sigma = G_j^\sigma$. The graphs of Figs. 1.44 and 1.45 are σ-equivalent, since they are symmetrically arranged in the same way, as represented in Fig. 1.46. The relation σ is indeed an equivalence relation since it is defined relative to the equality of the symmetric arrangements: $G_i^\sigma = G_j^\sigma$.

This relation is defined over each set $\mathscr{G}_n$, since if $G_i \in \mathscr{G}_n$ and $G_i \in \mathscr{G}_m$, where $n \neq m$, it is impossible to have $G_i^\sigma = G_j^\sigma$.

Each class of σ-*equivalence* is a part of the lattice $\mathscr{L}_n$; in each class every subset possesses a superior limit (see Sec. 3.3.), which is the union of the graphs of the subset. But the intersection of the graphs of the subset is not necessarily in the class: there is no inferior limit (each class is said to be a *higher semilattice*). Figure 1.47 represents such a class of σ-equivalence.

We shall represent by $\mathscr{G}_n^\sigma$ the set of the classes of σ-equivalence of $\mathscr{G}_n$. Each class of σ-equivalence may be represented by the symmetric graph which is its maximum. Therefore $\mathscr{G}_n^\sigma$ may be considered as the set of n-points symmetric graphs.

Like $\mathscr{G}_n$, this set $\mathscr{G}_n^\sigma$ is ordered by inclusion and has the lattice structure, which will be designated by $\mathscr{L}_n^\sigma$; two graphs are indeed σ-equivalent if they

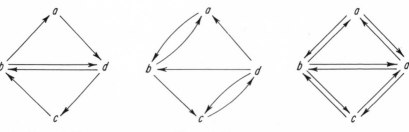

Figure 1.44   Figure 1.45   Figure 1.46

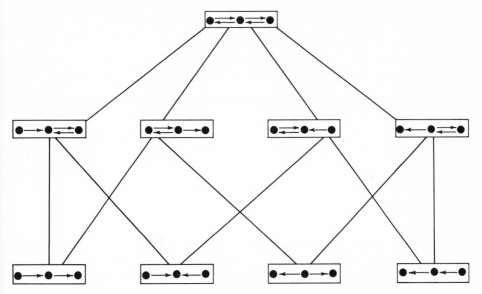

Figure 1.47

have the same set of *edges* (they differ by their arcs). We can therefore study the set of the $n(n-1)/2$ edges which can exist in an *n*-points graph.

If $n = 3$ and $X = \{a, b, c\}$, this set of edges is

$$\{(a, b), (a, c), (b, c)\}.$$

Figure 1.48 shows the lattice of the parts of this set and, at once, the lattice $\mathcal{L}_n^\sigma$.

8.5. Distances between Graphs

We have defined the distance between two parts of a set by the power of the symmetric difference of these parts (Sec. 4). But we have seen that the set of *n*-points graphs was isomorphic to the set of parts of the set of arcs of the complete symmetric *n*-points graph. This distance between two graphs $G_i = (X; V_i)$ and $G_j = (X; V_j)$ can therefore be defined as follows:

$$d(G_iG_j) = |V_i \oplus V_j|.$$

Theorems 1.4 and 1.5 are therefore valid for $\mathcal{L}_n$, by defining of course the union and the intersection of the two graphs of $\mathcal{L}_n$ by the union and the intersection of their sets of arcs:

$$G_i \cup G_j = (X; V_i \cup V_j);$$
$$G_i \cap G_j = (X; V_i \cap V_j).$$

The same notions can be applied to $\mathcal{L}_n^\sigma$ if the term arc is replaced by edge in the above discussion. Notice that the distance $d(G_i^\sigma G_j^\sigma)$ in $\mathcal{L}_n^\sigma$ *is not* equal to the distance $d(G_iG_j)$ in $\mathcal{L}_n$.

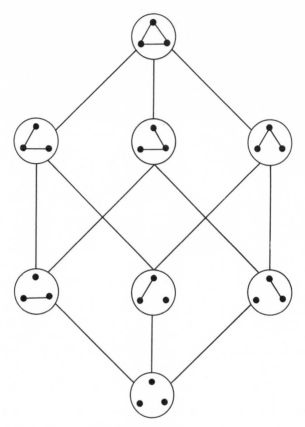

Figure 1.48

9. Various Types of Graphs

Up to now we have considered graphs which represent a correspondence Γ within a set X; this allows us only to represent a relation in an all-or-none fashion between, say, the members of a group. More complex phenomena are generally dealt with in social psychology. This is made possible by means of the theory of graphs. The various types of graphs which will now be considered are mathematically less studied than the graphs $(X; \Gamma)$. It should be noted, however, that the consideration of a more complex graph can to a large extent be reduced to the consideration of the graphs of the type $(X; \Gamma)$.

Simple graph. A simple graph is a graph $(X_0; \Gamma) = (X_0; V)$ such that there exists a bi-partition X, Y of X_0: $X \cup Y = X_0$, $X \cap Y = \emptyset$, and that any arc of V has its origin in X and its terminal point in Y:

$$(x, y) \in V \Rightarrow x \in X \quad \text{and} \quad y \in Y$$

or $\Gamma X \subset Y$ and $\Gamma Y = \emptyset$.

Note that $X \cap Y = \emptyset$ and $\Gamma X \subset Y$ implies
$(\Gamma X) \cap X = \emptyset$.

A simple graph is actually used to represent a
mapping Γ of a set X into a set Y which is different
from X. A simple graph is denoted by $(X, \ Y; \ \Gamma)$.
Figure 1.49 represents the graph of the correspondence whose table was presented in Sec. 2.5.

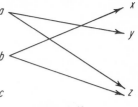

Figure 1.49

Valued graph. A valued graph is a graph $(X; \ V)$ to which is added a mapping v of the set V of the arcs into the set of real numbers. The *number* linked
to the arc (x, y) is $v(x, y)$ and is called the *value* of the arc; the function v is
the *valuation* of the graph (Fig. 1.50).

A valued graph allows us to represent the intensity of the relationships
within a group. Valued graphs will be greatly relied upon in Chapter 2, in
order to take into account the cost (psychological or financial) of the communications in a group.

If for whatever $(x, y) \in V$, we have $v(x, y)$ equal to a constant, the graph
has a constant valuation and can be considered as a nonvalued graph.

In a valued graph, a path is defined as in a nonvalued one, but the *length* of a
path is the sum of the values of the arcs of which the path consists. If a nonvalued graph is considered as a graph with a constant valuation equal to one,
the valued and nonvalued lengths of a path are identical. It may therefore be
more useful, for the sake of generality, to consider only valued graphs.

The notions of deviation and track are defined as in a nonvalued graph, on
the basis of the length, but this length is valued. Thus in the valued graph of
Fig. 1.50, the deviation $e(cb)$ is 2.5, which is the length of the path (cab),
though the arc (c, b) exists, with a value of $v(c, b) = 4$.

The computation of deviations and the method used to find the tracks in a
valued graph will be dealt with in Chapter 2.

Multi-graph. A multi-graph represents in a set X many types of relations:
$\Gamma, \ \Delta, \ \ldots$; it is denoted $(X; \ \Gamma, \ \Delta)$. A multi-graph allows us to take into account
the various psychological kinds of relationships in a group; a sociogram based
on many criteria of choice is a multi-graph. We represent a multi-graph by

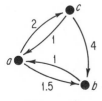

Figure 1.50

Figure 1.51

the use of different colors or different methods of writing, corresponding to the various relations Γ, Δ, . . . (Fig. 1.51).

Algebraic graph. An algebraic graph is a bi-graph (a multi-graph with two relations), with one relation, P, considered as positive and one relation, N, as negative and such that a pair cannot belong to P and to N at the same time (though it can belong neither to P nor to N):

$$(x, y) \in P \Rightarrow (x, y) \notin N$$
and
$$(x, y) \in N \Rightarrow (x, y) \notin P.$$

An algebraic graph is a very particular case of multi-graph, or else of valued graph, with the set of values reduced to $+1$ and -1.

In Chapter 3 we shall use complete symmetric algebraic graphs, such as that of Fig. 1.52, where the arcs represented by full lines belong to P, and those represented by broken lines, to N.

Marked graph. A marked graph is a graph of the type $(X; \Gamma)$, but where X is generally partitioned independently of the Γ function. A graphic sign distinguishes the points of the various parts (Fig. 1.53) in the sociogram of a mixed group. We often represent the girls by a circle and the boys by a triangle: this is a marked graph. The marking methods (numerical or by $\pm$) which were used above (Secs. 6.3 and 7.4) produce marked graphs, but this time take into account certain properties of the function.

The various types of graphs that we have briefly defined above can be combined in the same graph: for instance, a sociogram with choice and rejection, preferential order, and many criteria in a mixed group will be represented by a valued marked algebraic multi-graph.

Figure 1.52

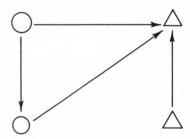

Figure 1.53

CHAPTER TWO

Communication Networks

1. The Problem

A social group can exist as a group only if its members communicate among themselves by means of verbal, written, facial, and other expressions.

This proposition is easily granted—but the fact is often overlooked that any communication, whatever its nature, requires a physical medium such as sound or visual waves, written documents, etc. Communication therefore implies more or less complex physical processes, and in many cases the physical environment will hinder or even prevent communication between certain members of the group.

This physical aspect of the process of communication occurs in all groups, but it is perhaps only in large and institutionalized groups that it appears clearly. In a large administrative service, the offices are placed in such a way as to facilitate direct verbal exchanges, personnel are assigned to carry documents from one office to the other, an intercommunication system is installed, and so on. On the national and international levels, we hardly need mention the importance of systems of telecommunication.

The set of physical conditions allowing communication within a group will be referred to as a communication network. It is but a generalization of the usual expression: telephone network, postal network, road network, etc.

The development of a network of communication in a group often is not based on valid scientific criteria. Nevertheless, the choice of which particular network is established matters to the group, since its life can be greatly affected thereby. Therefore, the psycho-sociological problem raised is the following:

in what way does the life of the group depend on the available communication network?

It is to the credit of Bavelas (1948 and 1950) and his school of research (especially Leavitt, 1951) that they have been the first to deal with this problem in a scientific, mathematical, and experimental fashion. Many mathematical* or experimental† works have since contributed to our knowledge, but without yielding a final solution.

It will be shown that a network can be represented by a graph, valued or not (Sec. 2). Bavelas' idea was to look for certain mathematical characteristics of the graph representing the network, and to examine experimentally their influence on the life of the group. However, the analysis of different works, and new experiments (Flament, 1956 and 1958a), have indicated that these characteristics of the network are insufficient to explain the phenomena; the task assigned to the group,‡ and particularly the relationship between the network and the task, must also be taken into account (Flament, 1958c).

It will be shown that at least certain aspects of a task can be represented by simple and multiple graphs (Sec. 3). This will lead to the study (Sec. 4) of the complex relationships among graphs—a problem for which there is no known equivalent in the theory of graphs. Although many problems remain unsolved, and perhaps unidentified, nevertheless it should be possible to describe mathematically any group activity wherever doing so will add new notions to the theory of graphs—notions whose exact nature can now only be guessed at. Further research in this line will be fruitful both for mathematics and for the knowledge of society.

The mathematical analysis and the experimental data are brought together in the last section of this chapter (Sec. 5). The mathematical complexity will appear disproportionate in comparison with the simplicity of the laboratory studies. But the mathematical analysis is not intended to explain the experimental results, any more than the laboratory study constitutes an end in itself; both, in different and complementary ways, provide some of the knowledge necessary to the study of natural, large, and complex groups.

2. Description of a Communication Network

2.1. Introduction

Let $X = \{x_1, x_2, \ldots, x_n\}$ be the set of n members of a group. Define over X^2 a mapping Γ expressing the possibilities of communication in the group:

* Especially Chandessais (1957); Flament (1959); Harary and Ross (1954, 1957); Luce (1950, 1951, 1952b, 1953); Luce and Perry (1949); Mason (1953, 1956); Ross and Harary (1952, 1955); Shaw (1954a).

† Especially Christie, Luce, and Macy (1952); Flament (1956, 1958a, 1961); Gilchrist, Shaw, and Walker (1954); Heise and Miller (1951); Hirota (1953); Luce, Macy, Christie, and Hay (1953); Macy, Christie, and Luce (1953); Mulder (1959a, 1959b, 1960a, 1960b); Shaw (1954b, 1954c, 1955, 1956); Shaw and Gilchrist (1956); Shaw, Rothschild, and Strickland (1957); Shelly and Gilchrist (1958).

‡ Leavitt (1951) seems to have noticed this aspect of the problem, but because of insufficient mathematical analysis, its importance was not brought forth. The idea was subsequently forgotten.

$(x_i x_j) \in \Gamma$ if and only if x_i can address a communication to x_j.

A communication network can therefore be represented by a graph, which will be designated by N:

$$N = (X, \Gamma).$$

If N is a communication network, an arc $(x_i x_j) \in N$ is called a *channel of communication*.

In many cases, N is a symmetric graph:

$$(x_i x_j) \in \Gamma \Leftrightarrow (x_j x_i) \in \Gamma,$$

but there are groups in which certain possibilities of communications are unidirectional (this is frequently found in a street network!).

We can either establish $(x_i x_i) \in \Gamma$, if the notion of communication with one-self is considered, or $(x_i x_i) \notin \Gamma$, if Γ is considered to relate only to the material exchanges of communication with a certain physical or temporal extension. In any case, the adopted convention does not matter too much.

2.2. Valued Network

In many problems, it is not sufficient to consider only the alternative that x_i can or cannot communicate with x_j. It is necessary to take into account the capacity of each channel, its accessibility for use, the time required and the cost of the transmission of a message in this channel, and so on. These numerical indications constitute *valuations of N*.

Instead of ascribing to N many systems of valuation, it is more convenient, when possible, to summarize them in a single system. Generally, whenever a unique valuation is used, it represents the *total cost* of the use of each channel.

The valuation of a channel can be either a firmly fixed constant or simply an average varying more or less at random (in relation with the communication process studied). But *if the utilization cost of a channel varies with the use that is made of it*, it is no longer legitimate to represent the network by a valued graph.

When all channels are equally valued, the common valuation can be set equal to one, and in fact the graph of the network can be considered only in its nonvalued form.

2.3. Connected Network

Suppose x_i wants to send a message a to x_j; if $(x_i x_j) \in \Gamma$, there is no problem, and the communication a from x_i to x_j is said to be *direct*; if $(x_i x_j) \notin \Gamma$, and if there exists in N a path

$$\gamma(x_i x_j) = (x_i x_{i+1} x_{i+2} \ldots x_j),$$

the points x_{i+1}, x_{i+2}, ..., can *relay* the message a from x_i to x_j, and the communication a from x_i to x_j is said to be *indirect*; finally, if no path $\gamma(x_i x_j)$ exists in N, the communication a from x_i to x_j is said to be *impossible*.

These statements reveal the importance of the notions of connectivity for the study of communication networks. In particular, *all imaginable communications will be possible, directly or indirectly, if and only if N is strongly connected.* The works of Luce on the connectivity of graphs (1950, 1951, 1952b, 1953) were carried out for the analysis of communication networks.

2.4. Bavelas' Centrality Index

Upon examination of the networks of Fig. 2.1, Bavelas (1950) notes that, intuitively, N_1 can be said to be more *centralized* than N_2, N_2 more than N_3, etc. He then defines an index of centrality, with which the four networks of Fig. 2.1 can be classified in a direction parallel to their order of centralization.

Bavelas' index of centrality can be defined from the deviation matrix associated with N: $E(N)$.

$$E(N) = x_i \quad \text{-----} \quad e(x_i x_j) \quad \text{-----} \quad s_i = \sum_j^n e(x_i x_j)$$

$$S = \sum_i^n s_i$$

For all $i = 1, 2, \ldots, n$, $s_i = \sum_j^n e(x_i x_j)$ is calculated; then they are summed:

$$S = \sum_i^n s_i.$$

The point index of centrality is then defined as $c_i = S/s_i$; the (global) *index of centrality* of N consists of the sum of the point centralities:

$$C = \sum_i^n c_i.$$

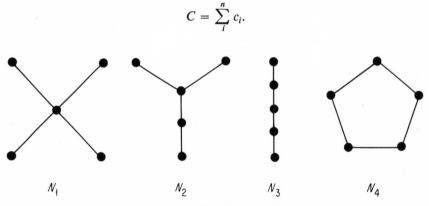

N_1 $\qquad$ N_2 $\qquad$ N_3 $\qquad$ N_4

Figure 2.1

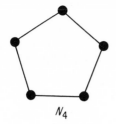
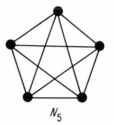

N_4 N_5

Figure 2.2

(Note that these operations are somewhat meaningless if N is not strongly connected, that is, if none of the deviations equals ∞.)

Table 2.1 shows the centrality of the networks of Fig. 2.1, as well as the centrality of the complete symmetric network of $n = 5$ points (N_5).

Table 2.1. CENTRALITY OF NETWORKS (FIGS. 2.1, 2.2)

Network	N_1	N_2	N_3	N_4	N_5
Centrality	26.4	26.2	26.1	25	25

The networks N_1 to N_4 are classified on the index as expected; but N_4 and N_5 have the same index of centrality, while it is not possible to accept that they are equally centralized (see Fig. 2.2).

The true significance of this index must then be examined.* On the basis of the definitions, we obtain

$$
C = \sum_i^n c_i = \sum_i^n \frac{S}{s_i} = \sum_i^n \frac{\sum_j^n s_j}{s_i}
$$

$$
= \sum_{i,j}^{n^2} \frac{s_j}{s_i} = \sum_i^n \frac{s_i}{s_i} + \sum_{i \neq j}^{n(n-1)/2} \left(\frac{s_i}{s_j} + \frac{s_j}{s_i} \right)
$$

$$
= n + \sum_{i \neq j}^{n(n-1)/2} q_{ij},
$$

where
$$
q_{ij} = \frac{s_i}{s_j} + \frac{s_j}{s_i}.
$$

But it can easily be shown that q_{ij} is at a minimum if and only if $s_i = s_j$; if this is so for all pairs (ij), the minimum index of centrality is obtained:

$$
c_{\min} = n^2;
$$

this is what is observed in N_4 and N_5 (Table 2.1).

---

* We have examined elsewhere the principles underlying the construction and validation of an index of a group structure (Flament, 1962a).

Consequently we are led to think that Bavelas' index measures specifically the *degree of disparity between the points of a graph.*

Let us be more specific about this notion. We know (Chap. 1, Sec. 8.2) that two graphs $G_1 = (X_1, \Gamma_1)$ and $G_2 = (X_2, \Gamma_2)$ are isomorphic if there exists a one-to-one function f between $X_1 = \{x_{11}, x_{12}, \ldots\}$ and $X_2 = \{x_{21}, x_{22}, \ldots\}$: $x_{2i} = f(x_{ij})$, such that

$$(x_{1i}, x_{1j}) \in \Gamma_1 \Leftrightarrow (f(x_{1i}), f(x_{1j})) \in \Gamma_2.$$

A graph N is said to be *automorphic* whenever it is isomorphic to itself, that is, if there is a one-to-one function f of X with itself such that

$$(x_i, x_j) \in \Gamma \Leftrightarrow (f(x_i), f(x_j)) \in \Gamma.$$

In the case of automorphism, we may have $f(x_i) = x_i$, but not for all i—because then f would be an identity function, in which case it would be preferable not to refer to automorphism. We could therefore define a degree of automorphism by taking into account, for each point x_i, the number of other points x_j for which there exists an automorphism f such that $f(x_i) = x_j$. To some extent, this is what Bavelas' index measures.

Indeed, if $x_j = f(x_i)$, we have, for any k,

$$\Gamma^k x_i = \{x_h, x_l, \ldots\},$$

and
$$\Gamma^k x_j = \Gamma^k f(x_i) = \{f(x_h), f(x_l), \ldots\};$$

that is,
$$|\Gamma^k x_i| = |\Gamma^k f(x_i)|;$$

but it is clear that

$$s_i = \sum_{j}^{n} e(x_i x_j) = \sum_{k} k \left| \Gamma^k x_i - \bigcup_{h=1}^{h=k-1} \Gamma^h x_i \right|;$$

therefore, if $x_j = f(x_i)$, we have

$$s_i = s_j \quad \text{and} \quad q_{ij} = \frac{s_i}{s_j} + \frac{s_j}{s_i} = \text{minimum.}$$

Through this analysis we have, we think, brought forth an unknown meaning of Bavelas' index, without pretending to have exhausted the content of this very complex index. Undoubtedly one may ask if it is too complex to be used efficiently in the description of a network.

3. Description of a Task in Communication Terms

3.1. Introduction

Two aspects can be distinguished in a group activity:

1. an *interindividual* aspect: communication of information (this term being understood in its general sense);

2. an *individual* aspect: formation from the informations held or received of new informations to be transmitted.

Only the first aspect concerns us here.

In a discussion group it is not possible, in general, to determine *a priori* all the informations used, or the exchanges that will take place in the group. The mathematical description of the group activity then becomes considerably more awkward. This problem will be considered later (Sec. 5).

In a work group, on the other hand, it is generally possible to determine *a priori* the informations and exchanges—that is, to describe the task in communication terms.

3.2. Primary and Secondary Informations

Let $A = \{a_1, a_2, \ldots, a_a\}$ be the set of α informations used in carrying out the task.

The set of *primary* informations consists of a part of A, that is, of the informations held by the group at the beginning of the activity. The other informations are *secondary*, that is to say, they are obtained while carrying out the activity from the pooling of many informations (primary or secondary). For example, the solution of a problem of arithmetic is a secondary information, obtained by pooling the elements of the problem, which are, generally, primary informations; in a firm the gross sales is a secondary information obtained from a set of primary (sales) or secondary (partial gross sales) informations. The peculiarity of the task determines the way in which a secondary information is obtained from the relevant informations.

Consider the set of parts of A:

$$\mathfrak{p}(A) = \{A_1, A_2, \ldots\},$$

where
$$A_i \in \mathfrak{p}(A) \Leftrightarrow A_i \subset A,$$

and the simple graph $P = (A, \mathfrak{p}(A); \Pi)$, defined by $(a_i, A_j) \in \Pi$ if and only if

1. $a_i \in A_j$ and A_j is a necessary and sufficient pooling for the elaboration of a secondary information, *or*

2. $\{a_i\} = A_j$.

(In the second case, any information derived from itself is conventionally considered as secondary; we will come back to this point shortly.)

In general, the degree of reception of a great many points of $\mathfrak{p}(A)$ will be null; in practice, they will be neglected.

3.3. Localization

Let $L_e = (X, A; \Lambda_e)$ be the graph representing the *localization of possible emissions.*

At the outset of an activity, every primary information is passed by one or more members of a group; if x_i possesses a_j, he can emit this information.

Similarly, if x_i proceeds to a pooling A_h, thus yielding a secondary information a_j, x_i will be able to emit a_j.

Consequently, we define $L_e = (X, A; \Lambda_e)$ by

$$(x_i, a_j) \in \Lambda_e$$

if and only if

1. x_i holds a_j at the beginning of the task, *or*

2. x_i obtains a_j from a part of A.

The first case corresponds to the initial localization of the primary informations; the second, to the localization of the pooling yielding the secondary informations.

Let $L_r = (\mathfrak{p}(A), X; \Lambda_r)$ be the graph representing the *localization of the necessary receptions*.

If x_i has to carry out a pooling A_h to obtain a secondary information, he must receive the group of informations A_h.

In general, a task is considered completed if certain members of the group have finally obtained certain informations; if x_i must finally obtain a_j, this information must reach him.

Therefore, we define $L_r = (\mathfrak{p}(A), X; \Lambda_r)$ by

$$(A_h, x_i) \in \Lambda_r$$

if and only if

1. x_i must finally obtain the information a_j, such that $\{a_j\} = A_h$, *or*

2. x_i must carry out the pooling A_h.

The first case corresponds to the final localization of informations; the second, to the localization of pooling.

Note that the localization of poolings appears twice in the analysis: in L_e and in L_r; this corresponds to the fundamental duality of the communication process: emission and reception.

3.4. Model of a Task

In a very general way, the initial localization of primary informations (partial graph of L_e, referring to the first case of the definition), and the graph of the pooling P constitute the *minimum definition of a task*. The localization of the poolings may or may not be given. If it is not given, the group will have to *choose*, among the possible localizations, the one which, for any reason, is the most appropriate.

There is another instance where a choice must be made by the group: if the same primary information is initially held by many members of the group, it is not necessary that each information-holder emit towards every receiver. The problem is the same whenever a secondary information is simultaneously obtained at several locations, and must be retransmitted.

Consider, then, the particular case of a task T meeting the three following conditions:

T_1: every primary information is initially localized at only one point;

T_2: the poolings of informations yielding secondary informations are localized *a priori*;

T_3: if a secondary information is retransmitted, it is through a pooling at only one point.

By definition,* if a task T meets conditions T_1 through T_3, the model $M(T)$ of this task is the graph whose associated matrix is

$$\| M(T) \| = \| L_e \| \cdot \| P \| \cdot \| L_r \|.$$

$M(T)$ *is the set of communications* (*direct or indirect*) *necessary and sufficient to carry out the task* T, as defined by the three graphs L_e, P, and L_r.

The matrices $\| L_e \|$, $\| P \|$, and $\| L_r \|$ are respectively of type $(X \times A)$, $(A \times \mathfrak{p}(A))$, and $(\mathfrak{p}(A) \times X)$, therefore, $\| M(T) \|$ is a matrix of type $(X \times X)$: it is associated to a function M of X with itself: $M(T) = (X; M)$.

From the definition of matrix multiplication (Chap. 1, Sec. 6), it follows that $(x_i, x_j) \in M$ if and only if there exists $a_h \in A$ and $A_k \in \mathfrak{p}(A)$ such that

$$(x_i, a_h) \in \Lambda_e, \qquad (a_h, A_k) \in \Pi, \quad \text{and} \quad (A_k, x_j) \in \Lambda_r.$$

If $(x_i, a_h) \in \Lambda_e$, it is implied either that x_i is the initial (unique, by T_1) holder of the primary information a_h, or that x_i has himself rearranged the informations necessary to obtain a secondary information a_h; there again, x_i is therefore the first holder of a_h, specified (by T_2) and unique (by T_3).

If $(a_h, A_k) \in \Pi$, it is that a_h is necessary to the pooling A_k (or that $A_k = \{a_h\}$, which comes to the same if we consider that any information is a secondary information elaborated from itself).

Finally, if $(A_k, x_j) \in \Lambda_r$, it is that x_j must carry out the pooling A_k (or receive a_h: $\{a_h\} = A_k$).

To conclude briefly: x_i alone holds the a_h that x_j needs for pooling; as a result x_i must transmit a_h to x_j. The transmission (direct or indirect) of all messages of this type is necessary to the performance of the task; it is also sufficient.

The matrix $\| M(T) \|$ can contain elements greater than unity: the number (zero, or positive integer) appearing in cell (ij) of $\| M(T) \|$ is the number of informations held by x_i having to reach x_j.

The graph $M(T)$ is therefore a multi-graph, with α components, each of which corresponds to one of the α informations. Depending on the case, we will consider either the multi-graph $M(T) = (X; M)$, or each component $M_h(T) = (X; M_h)$, $h = 1, 2, \ldots, \alpha$, or the uni-graph $M^*(T) = (X; M^*)$ defined by: $(x_i, x_j) \in M^*$ if and only if there exists at least one h, $1 \leq h \leq \alpha$, such that $(x_i, x_j) \in M_h$. The matrix $\| M^*(T) \|$ can be easily obtained from $\| M(T) \|$ by reducing to unity all nonzero elements.

If x_i initially holds an information, or obtains it himself through pooling, and if he must have this information at the final stage, we have

---

* This definition extends Lanzetta and Roby's (1955); but the matrices used here are not at all those of Lanzetta and Roby, who do not consider a secondary information as retransmittable.

$$(x_i, x_i) \in M^*,$$

but this is not a communication as in $(x_i, x_j) \in M^*$; in order to have homogeneous conventions (and for future developments, perhaps), it is worthwhile canceling all the diagonal cells in the various matrices associated with the model, if and only if it is agreed that the graph N of the communication network is without loop.

If any one of the conditions T_1, T_2, or T_3 is not met by a task T, the task has no clearly defined model.

However, the set of possible models of a task can be determined if all possible choices are considered, each being a possible specification of the task. In part, if T_1, T_2, and T_3 are met, it can be stated that the *set of possible models* of the task is reduced to a single element. Any work group can then be considered as facing a task T allowing a set $\{M(T)\}$ of possible task models; the group must choose one of the models and carry it out.

4. Optimal Organization

4.1. Introduction

Consider a group having to carry out a task of a fixed model $M(T)$, through a given communication network N.

$M(T)$ is the set of communications (direct or indirect) *necessary* (and sufficient) for the carrying out of T; N is the set of *possible* direct communications (from which the set of the possible indirect communications can be deduced).

The relations between $M(T)$ and N must first be examined in order to find out if it is possible to carry out T by means of N. If it is possible, it is generally possible in several ways; each of those ways will be called an *organization*. The *optimal organization* will then be chosen according to a certain criterion, which will generally be the global cost of operations under the organization considered. We will indicate a few elements of a solution of the problem of optimal organization, but, as will be seen, we are still far from knowing as much as would be desirable.

4.2. Possibility of Realization of a Task

If $M(T)$ indicates that an information a_h must be transmitted from x_i to x_j, this portion of the task can be carried out in a network N if and only if a path $\gamma(x_i x_j)$ exists in N.

It is useful, in view of subsequent developments, to state the above evidence in more elaborate language, due to B. Roy (1961).

Consider a graph $G = (X; U)$, U being the set of arcs of G. The μ-*transitive closure* of G is the graph $\mu(G) = (X, \mu(U))$ obtained from G by letting $(x_i, x_j) \in \mu(U)$ if and only if there exists in G a path $\gamma(x_i, x_j)$. A graph G and its closure $\mu(G)$ appear in Fig. 2.3. If we have the matrix $E(G)$ of the deviations of G, the matrix $\| \mu(G) \|$ associated with $\mu(G)$ can be obtained by reducing to unity all the nonzero and noninfinite elements of $E(G)$.

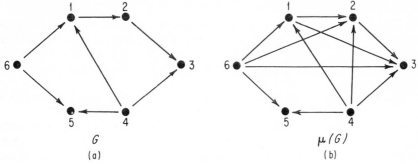

Figure 2.3

The operation μ is indeed one of closure in that it has the four properties defining closure (Berge, 1959, p. 13):

Monotonically increasing: $U \subset \mu(U)$;

isotonicity: $U \subset U' \Rightarrow \mu(U) \subset \mu(U')$;

idempotency: $\mu[\mu(U)] = \mu(U)$;

invariance of the empty set: $U = \emptyset \Rightarrow \mu(U) = \emptyset.$

The demonstration of these properties is straightforward.

The μ-transitive closure induces over the set of graphs of *n* points an equivalence relation: $G = (X; U)$ and $G' = (X; U')$ are μ-equivalent if and only if $\mu(G) = \mu(G')$. This relation is indeed one of equivalence, since it is defined by the equivalence over the closures μ, and since the closure μ of a graph is unique. Figure 2.4 shows a graph G' μ-equivalent to the graph *G* presented in Fig. 2.3.

The set of graphs of a μ-equivalence class constitutes a semi-lattice of union; indeed, *G* and $\mu(G)$ are μ-equivalent (idempotency of closure), and $\mu(G)$ is the superior limit of the class, since $G \subset \mu(G)$ (the closure is monotonically increasing). On the other hand, if *G* and G' are μ-equivalent, they are μ-equivalent to their union $(G \cup G')$; indeed, we have

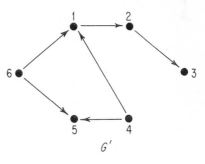

$$(x_i, x_j) \in \mu(G) \Rightarrow \gamma(x_i x_j) \in G \Rightarrow \gamma(x_i x_j) \in (G \cup G')$$

$$\Rightarrow (x_i, x_j) \in \mu(G \cup G');$$

hence, $\mu(G) \subset \mu(G \cup G').$

We also have

$$(x_i, x_j) \in \mu(G \cup G') \Rightarrow \gamma(x_i, x_j) \in G \cup G'.$$

Two cases must be considered:

1. $\gamma(x_i x_j) \in G$ (respectively: G') $\Rightarrow (x_i, x_j) \in \mu(G)$ (respectively: $\mu(G')$));

2. $\gamma(x_i x_j) \notin G$ and $\notin G'$: $\gamma(x_i x_j)$ is made up of some segments which belong only to G and of other segments which belong only to G'; but to each segment (x, y) of G corresponds a path $\gamma(xy)$ in G', since $\mu(G) = \mu(G')$; this second case cannot happen; therefore

$$\mu(G \cup G') \subset \mu(G)$$

and, finally, $$\mu(G) = \mu(G') = \mu(G \cup G').$$

But, in general, $\mu(G \cap G') \neq \mu(G)$; this happens if for at least one pair (x_i, x_j) there is not a single path $\gamma(x_i x_j)$ which is simultaneously in G and G'—which is frequent.

G_0 is a graph μ-*minimal* if *all* the graphs strictly included in G_0 are not μ-equivalent to G_0; in particular, if G_0 is μ-minimal, the deletion of *any* arc in G_0 yields a graph which is no longer μ-equivalent. It can be easily seen in Fig. 2.4 that G' is μ-minimal.

Consider a graph $G = (X; U)$; if $G_0 = (X; U_0)$ is (1) included in G; (2) μ-equivalent to G; (3) μ-minimal, then the family of arcs $V = U - U_0$ is said to be *deletable*: this family V can be deleted without altering any of the connectivity properties of the graph G. These analyses therefore complete the one carried out by Luce (1952b, 1953; cf. Chap. 1, Sec. 7.3.)

If we note that the μ-transitive closure of a graph N associated with a communication network is nothing but the representation of *communications directly or indirectly possible* in N, all the importance of the notions introduced by B. Roy can be seen. Research presently being carried out seems to indicate that they are indispensable for the development of the theory of networks, which will be briefly outlined in the following pages.

What has been stated at the opening of this section can now be restated differently: a task T can be carried out in a network N if and only if

$$M^*(T) \subset \mu(N).$$

Note that if N is strongly connected, $\mu(N)$ is the complete symmetric graph which includes all possible graphs; any task can then be carried out in N.

In the following paragraphs, it will be assumed that the task proposed to the group can be effected within the communication network available, and that the model of the task is perfectly known.

4.3. Finding the Optimal Organization

The model of the task, for each information a_h, reduces to $M_h(T)$; it can be summarized through the formation of two subsets of X: the set E_h comprising the points capable of emitting a_h (initial holders, if a_h is a primary information, or pooling points where a_h is obtained, if it is a secondary information), and the set R_h comprising the points receiving a_h (for pooling purposes or as a final localization).

The conditions T_1 and T_3 (Sec. 3.4) can be transferred by putting for any a_h

$$| E_h | = 1.$$

We have seen that these conditions were necessary for the unequivocal definition of the model of the task. However, it will be shown that, by virtue of an algorithmic device, the case $| E_h | > 1$ can be made the same as the case $| E_h | = 1$, in the problem of finding the optimal organization, and thus eventually provide a criterion for the choice of a model among all possible models.

We still do not know how to deal as easily with the case where the condition T_2 is not met.

The information a_h must be transmitted from E_h to all points of R_h; in general, this can be achieved in many ways, each constituting an organizational part (relative to a_h).

Each of these ways can be represented by a graph O_h, which is a partial graph of N:

$$O_h = (X, \Omega_h), \quad \text{with } (x_i, x_j) \in \Omega_h$$

if and only if the information a_h goes through the channel (x_i, x_j).

If a valuation representing the costs for the use of the channels has been ascribed to the graph N, the cost for the organization considered (for a_h) is nothing else but

$$c_h = \sum_{(x_i x_j) \in \Omega_h} v(x_i x_j).$$

The search for the optimal organization therefore consists in finding an organization O_h such that c_h is at its minimum.

(α) **The case where** $| E_h | = | R_h | = 1$. Let x be the only possible initial emitter of a_h, and y the only necessary receiver of a_h:

$$E_h = \{x\}; \quad R_h = \{y\}; \quad x, y \in X.$$

Among all paths $\gamma(xy) \in N$, the paths of minimum length must be found, that is, those whose cost of utilization is minimum; by definition (Chap. 1, Secs. 6.3 and 9), the minimum paths are the *tracks* $\theta(xy)$.

Let $\Theta(xy)$ be the partial graph of N, defined by: $(x_i, x_j) \in \Theta(xy)$ if and only if

Θ_1: $(x_i, x_j) \in N$;

Θ_2: $e(xx_i) + e(x_iy) = e(xx_j) + e(x_jy) = e(xy)$;

Θ_3: $e(xx_i) + v(x_ix_j) = e(xx_j)$.

THEOREM 2.1. *All the tracks* $\theta(xy)$ *of N appear in* $\Theta(xy)$, *and any maximal path of* $\Theta(xy)$ *is a track* $\theta(xy)$ *of N.*

Proof. A Bratton's theorem (1955) (cf. Berge, 1958, Chap. 13, Theorem 4) submits that any connected segment of a track is a track; therefore, if x_i is part of a track $\theta(xy)$, the segment (x, x_i) of this track is a track $\theta(xx_i)$ of length $e(xx_i)$; similarly, the segment (x_i, y) is of length $e(x_iy)$; hençe

$$e(xx_i) + e(x_iy) = e(xy).$$

Conversely, if the path $\gamma(xy)$ resulting from the succession of a track $\theta(xx_i)$ and of a track $\theta(x_iy)$ has a length $e(xy)$, this path is a track $\theta(xy)$ going through x_i. Therefore, a point x_i is part of a track $\theta(xy)$ if and only if the condition Θ_2 is met (x and y always meet this condition).

On the other hand, if a path $\gamma(x \dots x_ix_j \dots y)$ is a track $\theta(xy)$, by virtue of Bratton's theorem, x_i and x_j being located consecutively in this path, the segments (x, x_i), (x_i, x_j), and (x_j, y) are tracks, and

$$e(xx_i) + e(x_ix_j) + e(x_jy) = e(xy),$$

with $e(x_ix_j) = v(x_ix_j)$. Conversely, if x_i and x_j are each part of a track $\theta(xy)$, if Θ_2 is met, and if

$$e(xx_i) + v(x_ix_j) = e(xx_j),$$

the path $\gamma(x \dots x_ix_j \dots y)$, formed by a track $\theta(xx_i)$, the arc (x_i, x_j), and a track $\theta(x_jy)$ has a length

$$e(xx_i) + v(x_ix_j) + e(x_jy) = e(xx_j) + e(x_jy) = e(xy),$$

by Θ_2, and this path is a track $\theta(xy)$.

The condition Θ_1 can be included in Θ_3 by putting:

$$v(x_ix_j) = \infty \Leftrightarrow (x_ix_j) \notin N.$$

Finding the deviations in a valued graph. A marking method to find the deviations in a nonvalued graph was presented above (Chap. 1, Sec. 6.2). Now a generalized method will be presented.

To find the deviations from one point $x \in X$ to all other points of X, we use a double marking, $\{k; q\}$:

1. Mark x: $\{k = 0; q(x) = 0\}$;

2. If $y \in X$ is marked $\{k; q(y)\}$, consider successively all the $z \in \Gamma y$:
   (α) if z has not yet been marked, mark it $\{(k +1); q(z) = q(y) + v(yz)\}$;
   (β) if z is already marked $\{k'; q'(z)\}$ (we necessarily have $k' \leq k$), two cases must be considered:

   (β1) if $q'(z) < q(y) + v(yz)$, do not change anything to z's marking;
   (β2) if $q'(z) \geq q(y) + v(yz)$, change z's marking to
   $$\{(k + 1); q(z) = q(y) + v(yz)\};$$

3. Stop as soon as no point is marked at the step $(k + 1)$; we then get $e(xy) = q(y)$ for the marked points, and $e(xy) = \infty$ for the other points.

Practically, the marking is done in a table which is added to the matrix associated with a graph; for instance, for the graph N of Fig. 2.5, let us find the deviation of f:

$\| N \| =$

	a	b	c	d	e	f	g	h	i	j
a		4		2						
b			2					3		
c				6		3				
d	3							5		
e		2		6		1		6		
f			5							1
g					1	3				
h				4						2
i			4		2					
j							4	5		

$k =$

	a	b	c	d	e	f	g	h	i	j
0						0				
1			5							1
2				~~11~~			~~8~~ 5	6		
3	~~14~~			10	6				~~16~~	
4	13	~~18~~ 8							~~15~~	
5								11		
6										

$e(f.) =$	13	8	5	10	6	0	5	6	11	1

Practical construction of $\Theta(xy)$. We look for the set $\{e(x.)\}$ of deviations of x from the points of X, and the set $\{e(.y)\}$ of deviations of the points of X from y; we add term to term to obtain the $e(xx_i) + e(x_iy)$, and we retain the points which satisfy Θ_2. We then arrange these points x_i as a function of the deviations $e(xx_i)$, and we identify, for each point beginning with x, the arcs going from this point to the following points which satisfy Θ_3.

Example. Consider the graph N in Fig. 2.5, whose matrix is the following:

$$E(N) =$$

	a	b	c	d	e	f	g	h	i	j
a	0	4	6	2	9	10	9	15	7	11
b	11	0	2	8	5	6	5	11	3	7
c	9	6	0	6	4	5	3	10	9	6
d	3	7	9	0	7	8	12	13	5	9
e	13	2	4	10	0	1	6	6	5	2
f	13	8	5	10	6	0	5	6	11	1
g	14	3	5	11	1	2	0	7	6	3
h	7	9	11	4	7	8	6	0	9	2
i	13	4	4	10	2	3	7	8	0	4
j	12	7	9	9	5	6	4	5	10	0

We have to find Θ (ah):

	a	b	c	d	e	f	g	h	i	j
$e(a.) =$	0	4	6	2	9	10	9	15	7	11
$e(.h) =$	15	11	10	13	6	6	7	0	8	5
	15	15	16	15	15	16	16	15	15	16

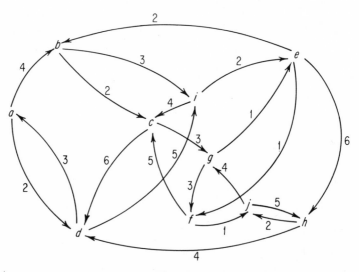

Figure 2.5

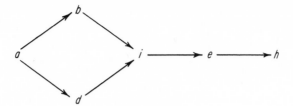

Figure 2.6

The points a, b, d, e, h, and i meet Θ_2.

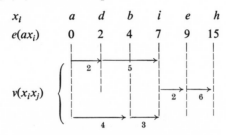

x_i	a	d	b	i	e	h
$e(ax_i)$	0	2	4	7	9	15

Hence, we have the two tracks $\theta(ah)$ (cf. Fig. 2.6):

$$a\ d\ i\ e\ h \quad \text{and} \quad a\ b\ i\ e\ h.$$

(β) **Case where** $|E_h| > 1$ **and** $|R_h| = 1$. If the information a_h is initially held at many points, it is sufficient that it be emitted in the direction of the point R_h by only one of the points.

For each point x_i of E_h, the minimum cost of the operation is measured by means of the deviation of x_i from the unique point y of R_h; x_i will then be chosen such that:

$$e(x_i y) = \min_{x \in E_h} \{e(xy)\}.$$

Once this choice has been made, we are brought to the preceding problem.

However, because of the cases where $|R_h| > 1$, it is useful to present the problem differently. From the graph $N = (X; \Gamma)$, build a graph $N_0 = (X_0; \Gamma_0)$, letting

1. $X_0 = X \cup \{x_0\}$, $x_0 \notin X$;
2. if x_i, $x_j \in X$, $(x_i x_j) \in \Gamma \Rightarrow (x_i x_j) \in \Gamma_0$;
3. if $x_i \in E_h$, $(x_0 x_i) \in \Gamma_0$ and $v(x_0 x_i) = 0$.

This construction will appear more concrete if we imagine an individual x_0 outside the group who alone holds the information a_h but can transmit it only to the members of the group which constitutes E_h; this transmission can be made without cost.

Finding, with N_0, the tracks from x_0 to y, $\{y\} = R_h$, is obviously the solution of the problem. We will denote the set of these tracks $\theta(x_0 y)$ by $\Theta_0(E_h; y)$.

There is another advantage to this method: if the relation

$$e(x_i y) = \min_{x \in E_h} \{e(xy)\}$$

denotes more than one point of E_h, $\Theta_0(E_h; y)$ yields the complete set of solutions through a single application of the algorithm.

Example. In the graph N of Fig. 2.5, we define $E_h = \{e, f\}$ and $R_h = \{a\}$. We have $e(ea) = e(fa)$. To obtain the complete set of solutions, one must then look for $\Theta(ea)$ and $\Theta(fa)$. Let us locate ourselves in N_0, and let us apply the algorithm. It is clear that for any $x_i \in X$,

$$e(x_0 x_i) = \min_{x \in E_h} \{e(xx_i)\}.$$

Hence the table:

	x_0	a	b	c	d	e	f	g	h	i	j
$e(e.)$		13	2	4	10	0	1	6	6	5	2
$e(f.)$		13	8	5	10	6	0	5	6	11	1
$e(x_0.)$	0	13	2	4	10	0	0	5	6	5	1
$e(.a)$	13	0	11	9	3	13	13	14	7	13	12
	13	13	13	13	13	13	13	19	13	18	13

and

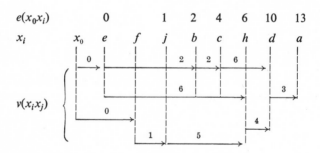

The solutions are the three tracks (cf. Fig. 2.7)

$$e\,b\,e\,d\,a, \qquad e\,h\,d\,a, \qquad f\,j\,h\,d\,a.$$

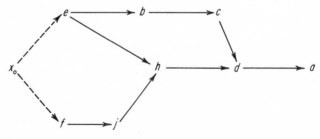

Figure 2.7

In order to obtain the three solutions, without using N_0, it would have been necessary to apply the algorithm twice.

(γ) **Case where** $|R_h| > 1$. Since the graph N_0 was introduced, we can always consider that $|E_h| = 1$; from now on, this will be assumed to be the case.

Moving from $|R_h| = 1$ to $|R_h| > 1$ is not at all analogous to moving from $|E_h| = 1$ to $|E_h| > 1$: it was not necessary that the information be emitted from all points of E_h, but it is necessary that all points of R_h receive a_h.

An arborescence (cf. Chap. 1, Secs. 5.6 and 9) must then be found with root x, if $E_h = \{x\}$, and containing *all* the points of R_h, including, if need be, other points from X. The sum of valuations of the arcs forming the arborescence is called *total length* of the arborescence. We must then find, among all the arborescences with root x and containing R_h, the arborescences of *minimum total length*. It is absolutely insufficient to consider only the tracks leading from $\{x\} = E_h$ to each point of R_h. Let $E_h = \{i\}$ and $R_h = \{h, g\}$ in the graph N of Fig. 2.5. Using the method described previously, it is found that $\Theta(ih)$ and $\Theta(ig)$ are each reduced to a unique track, *ieh* and *icg*. The arborescence of Fig. 2.8, with root i and containing h and g, results from the union of these two tracks; the total length of this arborescence is 15. But Fig. 2.9 shows another arborescence with root i, containing g and h, whose total length is 13; this second arborescence is therefore better than the first (in fact, it will be seen later that it constitutes the solution of the problem).

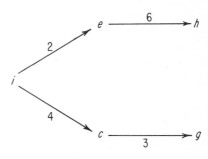

Figure 2.8

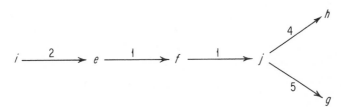

Figure 2.9

It must be said that presently no satisfactory general method exists. We will first examine the *Kruskal case*, mathematically very particular, but sufficiently important for us; then, we will look into the case where $|R_h| = 2$; finally, we will outline a generalization of the method for the solution of the case $|R_h| > 2$.

(δ) **Kruskal case.** Kruskal (1956) provides a solution to our problem in a very particular case:

K_1: the graph N is symmetric:

$$(x_i x_j) \in \Gamma \Leftrightarrow (x_j x_i) \in \Gamma;$$

K_2: for any i and any j, $v(x_i x_j) = v(x_j x_i)$. With these two conditions N can be considered a valued *nonoriented* graph; it is then appropriate to refer to *edges*.

K_3: two edges always have different valuations;

K_4: $R_h = X$.

Most communication networks are symmetric (K_1), and very frequently two mutual channels have the same valuation (K_2). On the other hand, many informations must be transmitted in the entire group (K_4). The Kruskal case is therefore of interest. Only K_3 can offer difficulties, particularly if N is not valued (that is, if all the edges have the same valuation).

Kruskal provides many algorithms leading to the discovery of a tree (non-oriented) containing all the points of X and of minimum total length; he also shows that this tree is *unique*. One with algorithms is the following.

Repeat the following operation as many times as possible: choose, among the edges not yet chosen, the one with a minimum valuation which does not form a cycle with already chosen edges. Once the tree is obtained, it is sufficient to orient the edges away from x, $\{x\} = E_h$, to get an arborescence of minimum total length with root x and containing all the points of X.

If N is not valued, K_3 is obviously not satisfied, but the problem is very simple. It is known (Berge, 1958, Chap. 16, Theorem 4) that the following properties are equivalent to characterize a graph G as a tree:

A_1: G is connected and when any edge is deleted, it is not connected any more;

A_2: G is connected and includes only $(n - 1)$ edges.

A_1 can be stated thus: $A'_1 - G$ is connected and μ-minimal (cf. Sec. 4.2). According to A_2 the total length of any tree of n points is $(n - 1)$, and therefore any tree is the solution to our problem.

In order to find all solutions, one can either look for all the connected μ-minimal graphs included in N, or arrange the edges of N in all possible ways, assigning for each ordering a value to the edges based on their rank and applying Kruskal's algorithm.

(ε) **Case where $|R_h| = 2$.** Let us denote by $\theta(x; R_h)$ any arborescence of minimum total length, with root x and containing the points of R_h. If $R_h = \{y_1, y_2\}$, any minimum arborescence $\theta(x; y_1 y_2)$ will be represented by one of the diagrams of Fig. 2.10 (where the arrows represent paths and not arcs). The last three diagrams reduce to the first when we let, respectively,

$$z = x, \qquad z = y_1, \qquad z = y_2.$$

The point z will be called a *branching of the arborescence*; it is evidently unique.

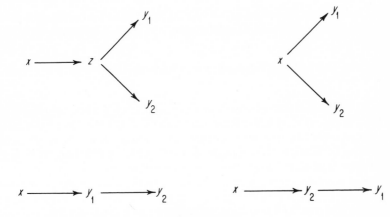

Figure 2.10

THEOREM 2.2. *In a minimal arborescence* $\theta(x; y_1 y_2)$ *with a branching z, the paths* $\gamma(xz)$, $\gamma(xy)$, *and* $\gamma(zy_2)$ *are tracks.*

This is evident, otherwise the arborescence would not be of minimum total length.

THEOREM 2.3. *If z is the branching of a minimal arborescence* $\theta(x; y_1 y_2)$, *two arbitrary tracks* $\theta(zy_1)$ *and* $\theta(zy_2)$ *share one and only one point in common: the point z.*

Proof. It is evident that z is common to $\theta(zy_1)$ and $\theta(zy_2)$. Suppose that it is so for z' also; the arborescence considered $\theta(x; y_1 y_2)$ has length (according to the preceding theorem)

$$e(x; y_1 y_2) = e(xz) + e(zy_1) + e(zy_2);$$

but

$$e(zy_1) = e(zz') + e(z'y_1)$$

and

$$e(zy_2) = e(zz') + e(z'y_2);$$

hence

$$e(x; y_1 y_2) = e(xz) + 2e(zz') + e(z'y_1) + e(z'y_2).$$

Now, suppose we have an arborescence consisting of the tracks $\theta(xz)$, $\theta(zz')$, $\theta(z'y_1)$, and $\theta(z'y_2)$; its length is

$$e(xz) + e(zz') + e(z'y_1) + e(z'y_2),$$

which is smaller than the length of $e(x; y_1 y_2)$, unless $e(zz') = 0$, that is, unless $z = z'$.

In order to systemize the notation introduced above, we will denote the total length of a minimal arborization by $e(x; R_h)$. In a way, it is the deviation of x from R_h.

THEOREM 2.4. *Given $\theta(x; y_1 y_2)$ with a branching z; x_i is part of a track $\theta(xz)$ if and only if*

$$e(xx_i) + e(x_i; y_1 y_2) = e(x; y_1 y_2).$$

This can be shown in a way analogous to the case of proposition Θ_2 (cf. Theorem 2.1).

THEOREM 2.5. $e(x_i; y_1 y_2) \leqq e(x_i y_1) + e(x_i y_2)$. *(Self-evident.)*

By means of Theorems 2.2 to 2.5, the following algorithm can be easily justified. We break it up in two parts: find $e(x; y_1 y_2)$; find the minimal arborescences $\theta(x; y_1 y_2)$. We proceed by successive estimates of $e(x_i; y_1 y_2)$, for every $x_i \in X$; the first estimate is evidently provided by Theorem 2.5.

Algorithm to find $e(x; y_1 y_2)$.

1. For every $x_i \in X$, calculate

$$e(x_i y_1) + e(x_i y_2),$$

which is the first estimate of $e(x_i; y_1 y_2)$.

2. Choose a point of R_h, for example y_1; we have

$$e(y_1; y_1 y_2) = e(y_1 y_2)$$

3. For every $x_j \in \Gamma^- x_i$, calculate

$$v(x_j x_i) + e(x_i; y_1 y_2).$$

Compare this value with the preceding estimate of $e(x_1; y_1 y_2)$; take the smallest value as the new estimate of $e(x_i; y_1 y_2)$.

4. End the process whenever no new value is obtained. The last estimate of $e(x_i; y_1 y_2)$ is an exact estimate.

Example. In the graph N of Fig. 2.5, find $e(i; gh)$. The algorithm is summarized in the following table, in which reproductions of a preceding estimate, excepting the first, are not indicated; it is not necessary to consider the descendants of corresponding points, since they have already been used. (*See next page*).

Algorithm to find $\theta(x; y_1 y_2)$.

1. For every $x_i \in X$, tabulate

$$e(xx_i) + e(x_i; y_1 y_2).$$

The x_i for which this value equals $e(x; y_1 y_2)$ are part of a track going from x to the branching of a minimal arborescence $\theta(x; y_1 y_2)$. Among the points thus obtained, we will consider branching z points such as

$$e(z; y_1 y_2) = e(z y_1) + e(z y_2)$$

x_i	$e(x_i g)$	$e(x_i h)$	$e(x_i g)$ $+$ $e(x_i h)$	Successive estimates of $e(x_i; gh)$					$e(x_i; gh)$
a	9	15	24				16		16
b	5	11	16			12			12
c	3	10	13		10				10
d	12	13	25				19	18	18
e	6	6	12				1̶2̶ 11		11
f	5	6	11			1̶1̶ 10			10
g	0	7	7	7					7
h	6	0	6			6			6
i	7	8	15				14	13	13
j	4	5	9		9				9

2. Find the tracks (cf. Sec. 4.3)

$$\theta(xz), \quad \theta(zy_1) \quad \text{and} \quad \theta(zy_2).$$

Example. Find minimal arborescences: $\theta(i; gh)$.

x_i	a	b	c	d	e	f	g	h	i	j
$e(ix_i)$	13	4	4	10	2	3	7	8	0	4
$e(x_i; gh)$	16	12	10	18	11	10	7	6	13	9
	29	16	14	28	<u>13</u>	<u>13</u>	14	14	<u>13</u>	<u>13</u>

The points e, f, i and j are part of a track going from i to a branching. Only j is a branching.

$$e(ix_i) \quad 0 \qquad 2 \qquad 3 \qquad 4$$

$$x_i \quad i \qquad e \qquad f \qquad j$$
$$\xrightarrow{\quad 2 \quad} \xrightarrow{\quad 1 \quad} \xrightarrow{\quad 1 \quad}$$

It can be seen immediately on the graph of Fig. 2.5 that the set of tracks $\theta(jg)$ and $\theta(jh)$ reduces to the arcs (jg) and (jh). Hence we have the minimal arborescence $\theta(i; gh)$, unique in this case, shown in Fig. 2.9.

(ζ) **Case where $|R_h| > 2$.** If the previous method were directly generalized by letting the first estimate of $e(x_i; R_h)$ be the value

$$\sum_{y \in R_h} e(x_i y),$$

it would suppose a unique branching z, as in Fig. 2.11. But the minimal arborescence $\theta(x; R_h)$ can very well be represented by Fig. 2.12.

In the case of Fig. 2.12, $e(x; y_1 y_2)$ must first be found, then $e(x; y_1 y_2 y_3)$ by taking as a first estimate $e(x; y_1 y_2) + e(x y_3)$. But in the case appearing in Fig. 2.13, we must first find $e(x; y_2 y_3)$. In the case of Fig. 2.14, we must begin with $e(x; y_1 y_3)$ . . . .

Since the case at hand is not known in advance, and since we may face many cases simultaneously (if there are many equivalent arborescences), all cases must be dealt with successively.

1. For every pair $y_i y_j$ of points of R_h, find $e(x_i; y_i y_j)$.

2. To each pair, add successively every point $y_k (k \neq i, j)$ of R_h, and apply the algorithm with, as a first estimate,

$$e(x_i; y_i y_j) + e(x_i y_k).$$

For each triplet $y_i y_j y_k$, three estimates of $e(x_i; y_i y_j y_k)$ are obtained (one from $y_i y_j$, another from $y_i y_k$, the third from $y_j y_k$); the smallest of these three values is exactly

$$e(x_i; y_i y_j y_k).$$

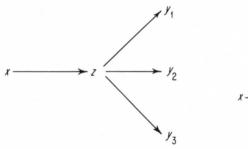

Figure 2.11

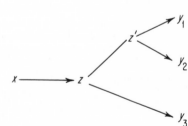

Figure 2.12

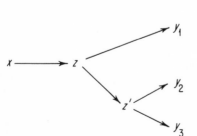

Figure 2.13

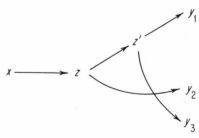

Figure 2.14

3. Move from triplets to squares, as we moved from pairs to triplets, and so on until R_h is exhausted.

It is clear that the method solves our problem; it is still more apparent that a more practical method is desirable.

However, note that if one has many analogous problems to solve (transmission of many informations: a_h, a_l, . . .), it may not be necessary to do the work every time; if $R_h = \{y_1, y_2, y_3\}$ and $R_l = \{y_2, y_3, y_4\}$, finding $e(x_i; y_2y_3)$ is useful for both problems.

(η) **Choice of an optimal pooling law.** Up to now, the task satisfying the condition T_2 (cf. Sec. 3.4) has been considered: the pooling law yielding a secondary information was set *a priori*. The case in which this condition is not met can now be dealt with. We have the following situation:

1. A subset A_h of informations is given; each of these informations is initially held by only one member of the group (we now know that we may always be brought back to this case).

2. The components of A_h must be pooled *at a certain point*, in order to obtain an information a_h.

3. This secondary information a_h must reach all the points of a set R_h.

4. The pooling point must be chosen in such a way that the cost of all necessary communications is at a minimum.

Let $A_h = \{a_1, a_2\}$, x_i being the only initial holder of a_1, and x_2 of a_2; and let $R_h = \{y_1, y_2\}$. Let us take z as a pooling locus. The operation can be represented through a multi-graph (a type of arc according to the informations at stake: three, here), as shown in Fig. 2.15.

Clearly, the secondary information a_h will be transmitted from z to R_h through one of the minimal arborescences $\theta(z; R_h)$. The information constituting A_h will proceed towards z by way of the tracks $\theta(x_1z)$ and $\theta(x_2z)$.

An algorithm can be given to find a *unique* point of optimal pooling. This is possible because the algorithm for finding an arborescence of minimum total length proceeds initially without specifying the root of the arborescence: we find $e(x; R_h)$ for every $x \in X$.

Let X_h denote the set of points at which an information of A_h is held. If A_h is pooled at point z, the cost of operations is

$$C_z = \sum_{x \in X_h} e(xz) + e(z; R_h).$$

Figure 2.15

All the terms in this expression are known through the previous algorithms; it is therefore sufficient to choose a point z_0 such that the solution is

$$C_{z_0} = \min_{z \in X} \{C_z\}.$$

It is then sufficient to study the tracks $\theta(xz_0)$ for every $x \in X_h$, and the minimal arborescences $\theta(z_0; R_h)$.

Example. In the graph of Fig. 2.5, we let $X_h = \{a, c\}$ and $R_h = \{g, h\}$; find a point of optimal pooling.

The values appearing below have already been calculated:

z	a	b	c	d	e	f	g	h	i	j
$e(az)$	0	4	6	2	9	10	9	15	7	11
$e(ez)$	13	2	4	10	0	1	6	6	5	2
$e(z; gh)$	16	12	10	18	11	10	7	6	13	9
C_z	29	18	20	30	20	21	22	27	25	22

The point of optimal pooling is therefore point b.

Finding the tracks and arborescence leads to the solution (unique in the present case) represented in Fig. 2.16. Note that e belongs simultaneously to X_h and to $\theta(b; gh)$; one would believe that a pooling at e would be more economical, but this is not so.

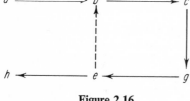

Figure 2.16

We must insist that this method can be used only if the pooling A_h should be at a *unique point* (a constant frequent in many groups, but not a general one).

Figure 2.17 shows a case where the solution by pooling at a unique point is impossible if we let $X_h = \{x_1, x_2\}$ and $R_h = \{y_1; y_2\}$: clearly, z and z' will each have to pool A_h, and direct a_h respectively to y_1 and y_2.

In the graph of Fig. 2.18, the same problem has two solutions: the above one, with a cost equal to 9; and a unique pooling in z, a_h being transmitted to y_2 from y_1; the cost of this solution is 10: it is not optimal.

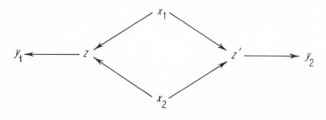

Figure 2.17

Consequently, the proposed method does not solve entirely the general case of our problem.

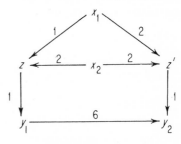

Figure 2.18

4.4. Other Aspects of the Problem

(α) **Duplication of messages.** Up to now we have implicitly considered that the cost of reproducing a message was discounted in the valuation of the network N. This is not always possible. In certain instances, the informations have the material aspect of *documents*, which will simply be transmitted if there exists only one receiver, but which will be reproduced at the branchings of arborescences. If the cost of reproduction is not negligible, this can modify the solution in that the cost of usage of an arborescence is then measured by the sum of valuations of the component arcs, *plus* a cost of reproduction at the branchings. The preceding algorithms can be slightly modified to include the additional cost: let ρ be the cost of duplicating a document; suppose $|R_h| = 2$. The first estimate of $e(x, R_h)$ was based on the assumption that x is a branching; therefore, instead of calculating $e(xy_1) + e(xy_2)$, we will calculate $e(xy_1) + e(xy_2) + \rho$, unless $x \in R_h$. The remainder of the algorithm is not modified.

In certain cases, however, the cost of duplication is not proportionate to the number of documents reproduced (in mimeographing, for example). In such an instance the following two extreme solutions present themselves.

1. The document is reproduced, one for each element in R_h; each copy is then carried over a *track*. It is no longer useful to look for an arborescence, since the common trunk will be followed by $|R_h|$ copies of the document, and the cost of usage will be multiplied accordingly.

2. The document is not reproduced, and the unique copy will go successively from point to point of R_h, in a certain order—for example, (xy_1y_2) or (xy_2y_1) The cost of the operation is measured by obtaining the sum of the deviations between two consecutive points in the chosen order. If the cost is thus calculated for each order, the most economical solution can be chosen. But the number of possible orders, $|R_h|!$, is soon enormous; an algorithm yielding a solution directly would then be useful. Note that this problem is very directly related to the one of Hamiltonian paths in a graph (Berge, 1958, Chap. 11; Camion, 1960; Flament, 1959a; Harary and Ross, 1954; Kruskal, 1956; Roy, 1961).

(β) **Relays.** The possible emitters and the necessary receivers of an information are defined together with the task; the relays are defined through the search for the optimal organization. Individuals who must rely on information may not be aware of its exact necessity, may be poorly informed of their role as "relayers," or may be little involved in the operation. For psychological reasons of this sort, we may then be brought to consider a cost of relaying the information in addition to the cost examined above.

We may come back to the techniques of analysis established in the preceding section while considering, not the valued graph N, but a series of valued graphs N_h, one for each information a_h. A graph N_h is the reproduction of graph N and of its valuations, with the relaying cost added in the following way. This cost may be divided into two parts, the relay-reception cost and the relay-emission cost, corresponding with the two aspects of the role of "relayer." The initial valuation of any arc (xy) will be increased by the relay-emission cost, unless if $x \in E_h$, and of the relay-reception cost, unless $y \in R_h$.

Note that if the network has a constant valuation, there is no problem: the shortest path is then always the one with the least relays.

(γ) **Saturation.** In the judgment of certain authors, whenever a great number of messages travel through the same point there may result, largely for psychological reasons, a saturation of that point and the deterioration of the group performance (Gilchrist, Shaw, and Walker, 1954; Shelly and Gilchrist, 1958).

When, for each information, there are many paths equally satisfactory, we can look for those which involve each in the transmission of only one information. But there may be instances where it would be interesting to use paths which are not tracks, in order to avoid saturation.

An additional cost, varying at each point as a function of the number of messages going through that point, should be introduced to make the notion of saturation more precise. The valuation of the network N varies then with the use made of it. It does not appear possible to adapt here the algorithms studied, both for the reason just mentioned and because these algorithms deal with the transmission of only one information at a time while saturation depends on the transmission of several informations.

(δ) **Temporal aspects.** Up to now, we have completely neglected the temporal aspects of the problem. These intervene at two levels.

First, certain modes of communication are such that the time required to emit or receive a message is considerable relative to the time required for transmission (verbal communication, in particular) and that the same subject cannot emit and receive many messages at the same time (e.g., it is not generally possible to communicate over the telephone with several persons at once). In such a case, the choice of the order of emissions and of the channels of communication may be initial to determine the temporal organization. For example, if x must transmit an information to y_1 directly, and to y_2 through z (Fig. 2.19), he will first address himself to z so that the latter can address himself to y_2 while x addresses himself to y_1. Generally, the transmission paths should be chosen so as to avoid, *at every moment*, the effects of saturation.

Figure 2.19

On the other hand, time may affect

the very definition of the task, which can include subtasks ordered temporarily (cf. Roby, 1962); this may involve important constraints in the search for the optimal organization.

Very closely related problems have been studied by Roy (1961) with the theory of graphs; his results should be adapted to the aspects peculiar to our problem.

(ε) **Risks of error in transmission.** It is not sufficient for an information to reach its receiver; it must reach him without having been altered by an error of transmission.

An information can be altered while going through a channel of the network as a result of a noise, or—perhaps more frequently—at the point of relay, because of the human failures of the "relayer." We then, once again, find the constraints already met.

However, the only way to have an effective guarantee that no error of communication will occur is to generate redundancy (cf. Miller, 1951, Chap. 12): to repeat the same information, through the same path, or through different paths (to eliminate risks of a systematic error). This means that the requirements for exactitude are generally opposite to the requirements of economy.

The mathematical study of these problems, which remains to be accomplished, will have to take into account Shannon's information theory (1948) and such works as those of Mason (1953, 1956) on network *feedback* phenomena which make possible the control of information.

Let us indicate still another aspect of the problem, which brings it close to questions of saturation: the arrival of many messages at the same point increases enormously the risks of error in reception (Egan, Clarke, and Carterette, 1956).

4.5. Inclusions and Distances between Networks, Model and Optimal Organization

Consider an n-member group having to carry out a task T in a network N.

In general, N is valued; when this valuation is neglected, a graph which we will denote by N^* is obtained.

The model of task T has already been defined (Sec. 3.4) together with the various types of graphs by which it is represented: $M_h(T)$, the graph of communications (direct or indirect) necessary in communication with an information a_h; $M(T)$, the multi-graph grouping all graphs $M_h(T)$; and $M^*(T)$, the graph obtained from the preceding ones without distinguishing the various informations. $M^*(T)$ will be denoted by M^*.

In a parallel way, the optimal organization resulting from the relations between N and $M(T)$ can be represented with the graphs O_h, in connection with the information a_h (these are the graphs discussed in Sec. 4.3); O, the multi-graph grouping all O_h's; O^*, resulting from O without distinguishing the various informations.

The three graphs N^*, M^*, and O^* are elements of the set of graphs of n points (cf. Chap. 1, Sec. 8); the relations existing among them in the lattice

$\mathcal{L}(n)$ can then be defined. In particular, the distances between these graphs can be studied. Recall Theorem 1.4 (cf. Chap. 1, Sec. 8.5):

If G and G' ∈ $\mathcal{L}(n)$,

$$d[G, G'] = d[G, (G \cup G')] + d[(G \cup G'), G']$$
$$= d[G, (G \cap G')] + d[(G \cap G'), G'].$$

Consider $d[N^*, (N^* \cup M^*)]$; in fact, this distance measures the number of arcs of M^* which are not in N^*: they are the necessary communications which absolutely cannot be carried out *directly.*

If $d[N^*, (N^* \cup M^*)] = 0$, then

$$N^* = N^* \cup M^* \quad \text{and hence} \quad M^* \subset N^*.$$

THEOREM 2.7. *If N is a graph with a constant valuation, and if $M^* \subset N^*$, then $O^* = M^*$.*

Proof. According to what we have seen (Sec. 4.3), the graphs O_h are tracks or minimum arborescences.

In the conditions of the theorem, if $(xy) \in M^*$, it is part of N^*, and the arc (xy) is the unique track $\theta(xy)$.

On the other hand, Berge (1958, Chap. 16, Theorem 7) shows that any arborescence is a tree, and consequently that any arborescence including k points has $(k-1)$ arcs (cf. Sec. 4.3(δ), property A_2). But, if $E_h = \{x\}$ and $R_h = \{y_1, y_2\}$, M_h is part of the arborescences consisting of the arcs (xy_i), $y_i \in R_h$; if $M^* \subset N^*$, this arborescence exists in N^*, and any minimum arborescence $\theta(x; R_h)$ will be of the same length; therefore this arborescence will be minimal.

If $M^* \subset N^*$, the result $O^* = M^*$ is generally true only if N has a constant valuation; however, it is also true in many other cases.

Consider now the distance $d(O^*, N^*)$ whatever may be O^*, equal or not to M^*. It measures the number of arcs of N^* which do not belong to O^*, that is, the number of channels in the network which are *not useful* for the performance of the task.

These notions and measures will be useful for the analysis of the behavior of the groups we shall now consider.

5. Applications

5.1. Introduction

In the applications to be presented, a disproportion will show between the mathematical elaboration and the concrete problems: there will be either too much, or not enough, mathematics.

In the experimental study of work groups, the *notions* of network, model, optimal organization will be used; the cases will be so simple as to eliminate the need of a mathematical development.

On the other hand, in the study of discussion groups or of large real groups (e.g., the management of a firm), the mathematics we have developed are clearly insufficient, owing to the complexity of the problems in such cases.

We think that a mathematical formulation nevertheless provides a link among the different studies; that the experimental study of work groups as a function of communication networks was born and developed under the impulsion of mathematical research; that in the study of more complex cases, our elaborations will either be integrated into a larger mathematical model, or constitute a fair approximation of certain essential aspects of the problem. In short, we think that our work is not completely useless (perhaps its main usefulness is that of inciting other researchers to make such analyses so that better ones will appear).

When a group having to communicate in a given network is considered, one may adopt either of two attitudes: (1) *A descriptive and interpretive attitude:* What is the spontaneous behavior of the group? How can it eventually be explained in reference to a mathematical model? This is the concern of experimental studies. (2) *A normative attitude:* How should the group behave in order to meet certain criteria of economy? This is the problem raised with a natural group such as the management of a firm. This last point will not be considered here; the preceding theoretical analyses give an idea of the importance but also of the complexity of the use of the theory of graphs in this field.

5.2. Experimental Study of Work Groups

This is the most studied problem in connection with communication networks.*

(α) **Experimental technique.** Groups are formed with n members each, where $n = 3, 4$, or 5; within these limits, the results do not seem to depend on n (Walker, n.d.).

Each individual is rated in a cell, and can neither see nor talk with the others. Openings in the walls of the cells make possible the exchange of written messages (see Fig. 2.20). The experimenter, by opening or closing these openings, can achieve the network of communication desired. Very generally, these networks are symmetric and strongly connected; a few studies have communication by telephone (Heise and Miller, 1951).

The task proposed to the subjects is of the following type (Leavitt, 1951, and most authors after him): there is a game with $(n + 1)$ symbols; each of the n subjects receives a list of the n symbols, the missing symbol being different from one list to the other. Therefore, only one symbol appears on all the lists; the task is completed when all the members of the group know the common symbol.

* Particularly Bavelas (1950); Christie, Luce, and Macy (1952); Flament (1956; 1958a); Gilchrist, Shaw, and Walker (1954); Guetskow and Simon (1955); Heise and Miller (1951); Hirota (1953); Leavitt (1951); Macy, Christie, and Luce (1953); Mulder (1959a; 1959b; 1960a; 1960b); Shaw (1954b; 1954c; 1956); Shaw and Rothschild (1956); Shelley and Gilchrist (1958).

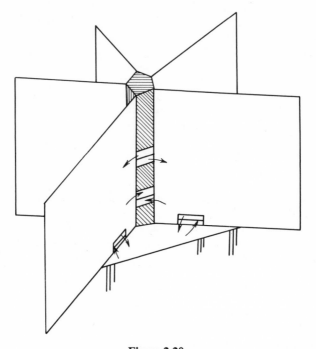

Figure 2.20

Example with $n = 5$ (Flament, 1956, 1958a): the six vowels of the alphabet A E I O U Y, are used; the five lists can then be

$$AEIOU-$$
$$AEIO-Y$$
$$AEI-UY$$
$$AE-OUY$$
$$A-IOUY.$$

A is the solution.

Each group is asked to solve successively many problems of the same type.

For each problem, the experimenter notes the number and the nature of the communications emitted by each subject in the direction of each of the others, as well as the time required by the group to reach the solution. Moreover, when the experiment is completed, the subjects fill out a questionnaire about the organization of the group, the choice of the leader, and the satisfaction with the work.

(β) **Choice of a task model.** In the task described, n primary informations are distinguished, each of which is initially held by a subject, and a secondary

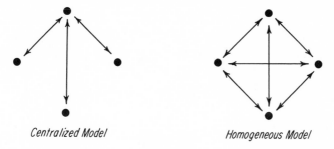

Centralized Model   *Homogeneous Model*

Figure 2.21

information, the solution, obtained through the pooling of the n primary informations, and which must be finally held by all the members of the group.

The pooling point is not defined; it is not even specified that it should be unique. Therefore, the task does not allow a unique model, but several among which the group must choose: n models with a unique pooling point; $n(n-1)/2$ models with two pooling points; . . .; one model with n pooling points. In all, $(2^n - 1)$ models.

In this set of models, two extreme types are distinguished:

1. *Centralized models:* a unique pooling point, this point being called the *centralizer*; there are n distinct models of this type.

2. *Homogeneous model:* every member of the group proceeds on his own to the pooling; there is only one model of this type.

These two types of models are represented by their graph M^* in Fig. 2.21. The other models are called *intermediary*.

Shaw and Rothschild (1956) examined 24 groups with four members each, eight of which worked in each of the networks of Fig. 2.22. The model eventually chosen by each group, after several trials, can be discovered through the analysis of the communications and of the questionnaires administered after the experiment. The results are given in Table 2.2.

Mulder (1959b) studied four- or five-member groups in the networks of

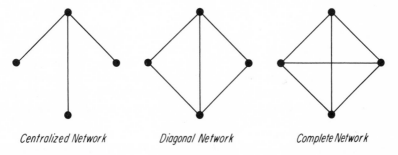

Centralized Network   *Diagonal Network*   *Complete Network*

Figure 2.22

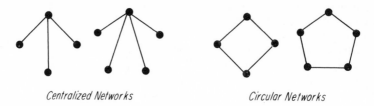

Centralized Networks   *Circular Networks*

Figure 2.23

Fig. 2.23. From the communications exchanged, he calculated a *decision centrality index*, approaching zero when a homogeneous model is applied, and approaching unity in the case of a centralized model. The results are shown in Table 2.3.

In order to understand these results, one must compare the models of Fig. 2.21 with the networks of Figs. 2.22 and 2.23. Intuitively, it can be seen that as a rule groups tend *to choose a model as close as possible to the network* in which they work. This is especially clear in the case of the centralized and homogeneous models. Going back to Sec. 4.5, we have in these cases the remarkable relations:

$$N^* = M^* = O^*$$

Table 2.2. CHOICE OF A MODEL AS A FUNCTION OF THE NETWORK

	Centralized model	Intermediary model	Homogeneous model
Centralized network	8	–	–
Diagonal network	1	5	2
Complete network	3	–	5

SOURCE: Shaw and Rothschild, 1956.

Table 2.3. MEAN DECISION CENTRALITY INDEX

	Centralized network	Circular network
Four subjects	.52	.30
Five subjects	.62	.11

SOURCE: Mulder, 1959b.

According to Shaw and Rothschild's comments, it is clear that what we have called an intermediary model is, in the case of the diagonal network, a model with two poolings localized at the terminal points of the diagonal.

An attempt can be made to specify the reasons for the choice between a centralized and a homogeneous model by considering the optimal organization, which would be defined in each network depending on the model chosen. We will retain the distance $d(O^*, N^*)$ and the cost related to O. Here the networks have a constant valuation, and the cost can be measured by the number of informations emitted and re-emitted. Table 2.4 shows the values resulting from this analysis.

Table 2.4

		Four subjects			Five subjects	
		Centralized network	Diagonal network	Complete network	Circular network	Centralized network	Circular network
Centralized model	Cost	6	6	6	7	8	10
	$d(O^* N^*)$	0	4	6	6	0	10
Homogeneous model	Cost	12	12	12	12	20	20
	$d(O^* N^*)$	0	0	0	0	0	0

The preferences between centralized and homogeneous models noted in Tables 2.2 and 2.3 can be completely explained from the data of Table 2.4 and the following rule:

The groups prefer the model in which $d(O^*, N^*) =$ minimum; in the case of equality, the model with a minimum cost is preferred.

This by no means implies that the groups reach a decision after having carried out a conscious analysis of the mathematical characteristics of the various possibilities.

But the results of the whole analysis justify the assumption of the following spontaneous behaviors: at the beginning, every subject emits messages in all available channels; the poolings are carried out at the points where the spontaneous conveyance of informations is possible; and the first step is reproduced with the secondary information; then, things are normalized. Unless communications disappear, the principles of economy regain their importance, but within the framework set in the first phase.

This analysis accounts fairly well for the known phenomena, but these are too few in number and too undiversified (too few types of networks have been used) to make possible any further analysis.

(γ) **Optimal organization and effective organization.** Consider a group which has to carry out a model of a task (either chosen by itself or imposed by the experimenter) in a given network of communication. In such a case, we know how to determine the optimal organization—in particular, the minimum cost of realization, measured here in terms of the number of communications. In fact, the group could adopt an *effective organization different* from the optimal organization. We shall discuss the effective cost.

It is clear that in all cases the *effective cost cannot be lower than the minimum cost*—by definition. It is therefore essential to evaluate the *efficiency* of a group through a comparison of the effective and minimum costs. However, most authors deal only with the effective cost, and with it establish differences in the efficiency of groups.

But in our experiments (Flament 1956, 1958a) and through our discussion of Leavitt's (1951) results (cf. Flament, 1958c), it was possible to show that *the ratio of effective cost to minimum cost* approaches unity towards the end of the experiments, if these last long enough, with all the groups, whatever the network. In all the networks examined, the efficiency tends equally toward the maximum. Therefore, the gross difference in performance observed among networks does not at all correspond to a psycho-social phenomenon; it simply results from the strict impossibility of doing otherwise once a network and a task model are given.

The real psycho-social phenomenon takes place at the level of the choice of the model (when the model is not dictated by the definition of the task). As we have seen, an expensive model can be chosen if it is the only one implying an organization such that $O^* = N^*$.

On the other hand, groups become equal in efficiency only after a certain period of exercise in the network; previous to that, things are different from one network to the other; this is what we shall now discuss.

(δ) **Model-network isomorphism.** Five-subject groups have been put to work in centralized and complete networks and the centralized or homogeneous model (Fig. 2.24) imposed upon them according to the plan shown in Table 2.5 (Flament, 1958a).

Table 2.5

	Centralized network	Complete network
Centralized model	$d[N^*, (N^* \cup M^*)] = 0$ $d(O^*, N^*) = 0$	$d[N^*, (N^* \cup M^*)] = 0$ $d(O^*, N^*) = 12$
Homogeneous model	$d[N^*, (N^* \cup M^*)] = 12$ $d(O^*, N^*) = 0$	$d[N^*, (N^* \cup M^*)] = 0$ $d(O^*, N^*) = 0$

We notice immediately that there is ismomorphism between centralized network and centralized model, and between complete network and homogeneous model; that is: $N^* = M^*$. Hence, according to Theorem 2.7, applicable in the present case, $O^* = M^* = N^*$; this is what is conveyed by the distances equal to zero in the corresponding cells of Table 2.5. In the two

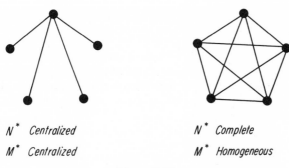

N^* *Centralized* N^* *Complete*

M^* *Centralized* M^* *Homogeneous*

Figure 2.24

other cells, there is *nonisomorphism* between network and model, but in a different way: in the complete-network, centralized-model cell, there is no channel missing in the network with respect to the model (all communications are direct), but there are twelve useless channels to achieve the optimal organization in the network. On the contrary, in the centralized-network, homogeneous-model cell, twelve channels are missing, and the corresponding communications must be relayed, but the optimal organization uses all the channels of the network. In the first case, there is nonisomorphism because of an *excess of channels*, in the other, because of a *lack of channels*.

To complete the description, we must also note the following. (1) In the present case of nonisomorphism because of a lack of channels, all the indirect communications must be relayed through the *same* point, the central point of the centralized network, which is an articulation point for all pairs of points in the graph. Therefore, there are risks of *saturation*. (2) In the case of a centralized model, the groups were instructed that the pooling point (*centralizer*) had to be unique, but they had to choose this point. In a centralized network, the central point of the network commends itself as centralizer, and in fact *all* the groups have made this choice (the values of Table 2.5 were calculated under this hypothesis). In a homogeneous network, any point can be chosen, the network being totally automorphic.

Figure 2.25 shows the evolution of the efficiency measured by the ratio effective cost/minimum cost for the problems solved successively by the groups. The curves are experimental, but were smoothed up once the statistical analysis had been carried out. Table 2.6 completes the results by showing the analysis of the content of the messages throughout the first problem.

Initially, the efficiency is already weaker in a centralized model than in a homogeneous model: the reason is the necessity of exchanging messages related to the choice of a centralizer, as shown by the relative importance of the organizational communications (Table 2.6). But for every model *the isomorphic situation is the most efficient*. The relative loss of efficiency in nonisomorphic situations must be analyzed in terms of the type of nonisomorphism. When *nonisomorphism results from an excess of channels*, the inefficiency comes from the unnecessary use of useless channels, as shown by the relative importance of redundant communications (Table 2.6) and by the comparison

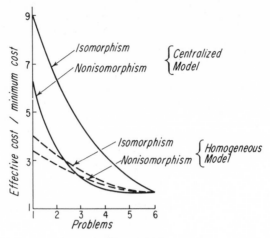

Figure 2.25

Table 2.6. CONTENT ANALYSIS OF THE COMMUNICATIONS DURING THE
FIRST PROBLEM

Model	Centralized		Homogeneous	
Network	Centralized	Complete	Centralized	Complete
Necessary and sufficient communications (=minimum cost)	8	8	20	20
Redundant communications	20	<u>36</u>	28	28
Requests for information	5	7	13	8
Organizational communications	<u>14</u>	<u>11</u>	7	0
Various communications	6	7	6	11
Total (=effective cost)	53	69	74	67

of the routes of communication in the two situations with a centralized model (Table 2.7). When *nonisomorphism results from a lack of channels*, the difficulties come from the malfunctioning of the relays, doubtless owing to saturation; this appears in the relative importance of the requests for information (Table 2.6). In fact, this difficulty persists for quite a while, and the importance of the requests for information in nonisomorphism by lack of channels is the only characteristic of Table 2.6 which also appears in the analogous tables corresponding to the subsequent problems (not presented here).

Table 2.7. Route of Communications in a Centralized Model
(Average over All Groups and All Problems)

Communications	Centralized network	Complete network
Centralizer ⟷ peripheral	20	18
Peripheral ⟷ peripheral	–	8

5.3. Experimental Study of Discussion Groups

Three-member discussion groups in the centralized and complete networks of Fig. 2.26 have been studied by Shaw, Rothschild, and Strickland (1957) and Flament (1961).

The subjects are presented, in varying quantities, with short aural or visual stimuli. They are asked to make an estimate of the number of stimuli. In general, they do not give the same estimate; they must then converse among themselves in order to reach a common estimate.

It is clear that the process of communication resulting from this situation cannot be described by means of a task model, in the strict sense we have given to this notion. However, it is possible to describe the process of communication in terms for which mathematization is still insufficient.

In most cases, two of the three subjects make initial estimates very close to one another, while the third subject initially gives a very different one. Let A and B denote the first two subjects, and X, the *deviant* third.

Centralized Network   Complete Network

Figure 2.26

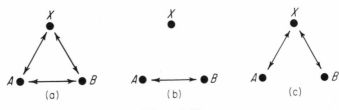

Figure 2.27

According to Festinger's theories (1950), it is possible to describe the processes of spontaneous communication, that is, of communication taking place outside the material constraints of a particular network. *Three phases* can be distinguished:

1. general exchange of information on each one's initial estimate; this phase is represented diagramatically in Fig. 2.27(a);
2. the forming of a majority by the subjects *A* and *B* who have slightly different opinions [Fig. 2.27(b)];
3. influence of the majority *AB* over the deviant *X* [Fig. 2.27(c)].

On the other hand, it is possible, from an idea of Deutsch and Gerard (1955), to distinguish *two types* of communications influencing someone's opinion:

1. *Informational* influence: someone's opinion provides an indirect information about reality, and this information is logically integrated with the subject's initial opinion, which is consequently modified (Flament, 1959b).
2. *Normative* influence: the subject adopts someone's opinion in order not to break *affectively* with him.

We can acknowledge that

(a) a *small* difference of opinion will be reduced by an informational influence alone as well as by normative influence;
(b) if two individuals reach an agreement through normative influences, they will have a group sentiment stronger than if they do so through informational influences alone;
(c) the normative influence by the members of a group on an outside individual will be as efficient as the group sentiment is strong;
(d) in a network of communication, the informational influence can be relayed, while the normative influence of a communication disappears when the latter is relayed.

Consider now the individuals *A*, *B*, and *X* defined above when they are in the networks of Fig. 2.26. Figure 2.28 shows the three possible cases.

Situation (α) is used as a control.

In (β) and (γ), the phase consisting in the exchange of information [Fig. 2.27(a)] is disturbed, but, no doubt, only negligibly.

In (β), the formation of the majority *AB* is not hampered and will take

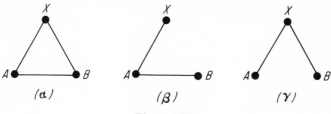

Figure 2.28

place under normative influence. The influence of the majority AB on the deviant X will be impeded by the absence of the channel BX, but A will speak in the name of a group (AB) with a strong group feeling, and will strongly influence X.

In (γ), the normative influence will not operate in the formation of the majority AB, but, differences of opinion between A and B being small, the informational influence, relayed by X, will be efficient. The influence of A and B on X can take effect without difficulty, but from a weak group, and without efficiency.

Through this analysis, it is possible to state that the initial difference of opinion will be reduced

(a) between A and B, approximately equal in (α), (β) and (γ);

(b) between X and A or B, approximately equal in (α) and (β), and smaller in (γ).

The experimental results of Table 2.8 completely support these predictions.

Table 2.8. REDUCTION OF THE INITIAL DIFFERENCE

	Between X and A	Between X and B	Between A and B
(α)	1.41	1.41	0.35
(β)	1.46	1.44	0.28
(γ)	1.21	1.21	0.29

SOURCE: Flament, 1961.

Clearly, these analyses could be generalized and mathematicized; however, it appears to us that this is not yet desirable, since our knowledge on the processes of social influence has not been sufficiently established.

It is appropriate at this point to summarize French's theory (1956) of which certain mathematical aspects have been developed by Harary (1959c). French assumes that measurable *power* relationships exist between the members of a group considered pairwise; the set can be represented by means of an oriented and valued graph. If the influence processes occur in a communication network, French assumes that the power of x over y takes effect only if the channel (xy) exists in the network. The possibility of relaying informational influence, it seems to us, is then neglected. This aspect of the phenomenon can easily be taken into account by considering that the power of x over y takes effect inversely with the deviation $e(xy)$. The formulas would be of the same mathematical type as those used by Harary (1959a) for the study of sociometric status.

CHAPTER THREE

Balancing Processes

1. The Problem

Let A be a man, H a top hat, and C a necktie. This man greatly likes to wear a top hat, and greatly dislikes to wear a necktie; but he knows that the top hat is worn with a necktie: his situation is very unpleasant!

It can be said that a *positive relationship* exists between A and H, a *negative* one between A and C, and a *positive* one between H and C. By representing the positive relationships by full lines, and the negative ones by broken lines, we obtain Fig. 3.1(a).

In order to get out of this unpleasant situation, Mr. A has several choices: he can accept the wearing of a tie, then the negative relationship AC becomes positive [Fig. 3.1(b)]; or he can give up the idea of wearing the top hat, then AH becomes negative; or he can even convince himself that a top hat can be worn without a tie: HC becomes negative [Fig. 3.1(c)].

Now let A again be a man, and B his wife. A dislikes wearing a tie, but his wife B likes him to wear one. Finally let us suppose that husband and wife wish to please one another. This situation is formally identical to the preceding one; it is represented in Fig. 3.1(a), by replacing H by B.

Finally consider three individuals, A, B, and C, amongst whom exist *friendly* or *hostile* relationships. According to popular wisdom, "The friends of my friends are my friends," which is represented in Fig. 3.2(a), and also, "The friends of my enemies are my enemies" [Fig. 3.2(b)]. Popular wisdom sometimes says, "The enemies of my enemies are my friends," which corresponds again to Fig. 3.2(b), but it is also said, "Divide and rule" [Fig. 3.2(c)].

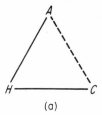 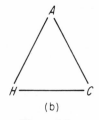 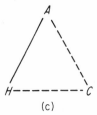

(a)   (b)   (c)

Figure 3.1

The latter situation is not very satisfactory for the dominated enemies, since they soon say, "Unity is strength."

This quick examination of a few cases, without pretending to be systematic, suggests that if positive or negative relationships exist between one person and two objects, or between two persons and one object, or between three persons, this is sufficient to define certain situations which are pleasant, and others which are not.

The systematic formulation of the problem comes from Heider (1946), and its mathematization from Cartwright and Harary (1956).

Clearly, in Figs. 3.1 and 3.2, the problem was translated into terms of *algebraic graphs* (cf. Chap. 1, Sec. 9). Such graphs therefore must show what characterizes the satisfactory situations and the others. From three-point graphs, we must also generalize to *n*-point graphs.

The psychology of the situations above requires that if the situation is not satisfactory, it tends towards a satisfactory situation. We shall therefore speak of *balanced or unbalanced graphs.* Apostel (1957) has suggested a general theory of the balance of a graph—a theory undoubtedly too general to be of great utility here.

After having distinguished the balanced from the unbalanced graphs, we shall try to determine, for the latter, *a degree of balance* which will allow us to classify them.

Finally, we will try to determine which *balancing processes* enable one to pass from an unbalanced to a balanced graph.

It will be seen that the theory of graphs enables us at least to approach this problem of group dynamics. It is often thought that the methods of modern

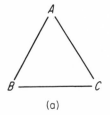 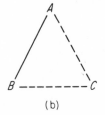 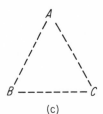

(a)   (b)   (c)

Figure 3.2

algebra, and particularly the theory of graphs, can be useful only for a *static description of structures*. We shall show that this is not so.

2. Definition of the Balance of a Graph

(D_1) A *complete algebraic graph* is a symmetric graph, such that between any two points there is a *positive or a negative edge*.

If X is the set of the n points of the graph, P the set of the positive edges, and N the set of the negative edges, a complete algebraic graph is represented by $G = (X; P, N)$ with $P \cap N = \emptyset$ (an edge cannot be simultaneously positive and negative); and $P \cup N = \{$the set of the pairs of distinct points$\}$.

The graphs of Figs. 3.3 and 3.4 are algebraic graphs, but only that of Fig. 3.3 is complete. We have

$$P = \{(ab), (ac), (ae), (bd), (be), (ce), (df), (ef)\},$$

$$N = \{(ad), (af), (bc), (bf), (cd), (cf), (de)\};$$

we do have the $n(n - 1)/2 = 15$ pairs of distinct points.

In an algebraic graph, chains and cycles are defined notwithstanding the sign of the component edges.

(D_2) The *sign of a chain or of a cycle* is the product of the signs of the component edges, the product being defined by the following multiplication table:

	+	−
+	+	−
−	−	+

It is the sign rule of classical algebra.

Put $s(xy)$ as the sign of the edge (xy), and $s[\gamma(xy)]$ as the sign of the chain $\gamma(xy)$.

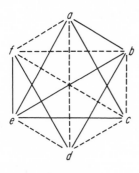

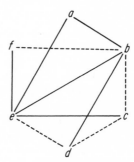

Figure 3.3   **Figure 3.4**

Thus in Fig. 3.3 definition D_2 gives, for example,

$$s[\gamma(abed)] = s(ab) \times s(be) \times s(ed) = (+) \times (+) \times (-) = (-).$$

(D_3) A cycle of length 3, or *triangle*, is balanced if and only if its sign is *positive*.

It could be easily verified that this definition covers exactly the pleasant situations outlined at the beginning of this chapter. In practice, it is seen that, by connecting definitions D_2 and D_3, a triangle is balanced if and only if it has zero or two negative edges; it is not balanced if it has one or three negative edges.

(D_4) *A complete algebraic graph is balanced if and only if all its triangles are balanced.*

Harary (1953a) suggests another definition:

(D_5) *A complete algebraic graph is balanced if and only if all its cycles are positive.*

Clearly D_5 implies D_4, since a balanced triangle is a positive cycle. It will be shown later (Theorem 3.2) that in fact these two definitions are equivalent. Definition D_4 has the advantage of being closer to the intuition we have of concrete situations, such as those analyzed at the beginning of this chapter. Harary's definition (D_5) has the advantage of being more easily applicable to the study of the balance of incomplete graphs (such as that of Fig. 3.4).

Other types of balance. Harary (1955) proposes two restricted notions of a graph: *local balance* and *m-order balance*.

A graph is locally balanced at point x if and only if all the cycles passing through x are positive. If a graph is locally balanced at all points $x \in X$, it is balanced according to D_5.

A graph is m-balanced if all its cycles of length inferior or equal to m are positive. If a complete algebraic graph is 3-balanced, it is so according to D_4.

We can also consider the balance of algebraic graphs which are nonsymmetric, incomplete, or valued.

If the graph is incomplete, it is easier to define balance by D_5, for it may well be that the graph contains no triangle. Or the graph is considered as complete, but with three types of edges, positive, negative, and null, and it is assumed that a triangle having at least one null edge is always balanced.

If the graph is nonsymmetric, we will talk of *circuit* instead of *cycle*, and the same definitions will be used.

One might think that a valued algebraic graph is necessary to represent psycho-social reality, if it is to take into account the degree of intensity of interpersonal relationships. But in fact it then seems hardly possible to define the balance of the graph, not for mathematical but for psychological reasons. If the relationship AB is $+3$, the relationship BC is -4, what should the AC relationship be in order that the triangle be balanced? The psychological hypotheses are wanting, or rather they are numerous and little justified.

Reflection, observation, or experimentation should first suggest a definition corresponding to facts, and then mathematics will deal with it.

In any case, we consider here only complete algebraic graphs, in the sense of D_1, balance being defined by D_4.

Harary's works (1953, 1955) and that of Abelson and Rosenberg (1958) show that the results obtained on the balance of complete algebraic graphs can easily be applied to other cases, and that this detour is often more useful than direct study.

3. Characteristics of Balanced Graphs

By means of definition D_4 a graph can be identified as balanced or unbalanced. However, the task tends to be tedious, and it is desirable to establish various properties of balanced graphs, which enable one to identify the latter more easily, while bringing forth certain deep meanings of the definition.

Theorem 3.1 is from Harary (1953) to the extent that he starts from D_5 rather than from D_4.

THEOREM 3.1. $G = (X; P, N)$ *is a balanced complete algebraic graph if and only if there exists a bipartition of X into X_1 and X_2 (one of these subsets can be empty) such that*

$$P \subset X_2^2 \cup X_1^2 \quad \text{and} \quad N \subset X_1 \cdot X_2.$$

In other words, X is divided into two classes, X_1 and X_2, and all the intraclass edges are positive, all the interclass edges being negative.

Proof of necessity. Let $a \in X$, an arbitrary but fixed point. Consider two points x and $y \in Pa$ (Fig. 3.5). We state that $(xy) \in P$, otherwise the triangle (axy) will be negative, since only $s(xy)$ would be negative. Consider two points x' and $y' \in Na$. We stated that $(x'y') \in P$, otherwise the triangle $(ax'y')$ would be negative, since its three edges would be negative. Finally, we state that $(yy') \in N$, otherwise the triangle (ayy') would be negative, since (ay) is positive and (ay') negative.

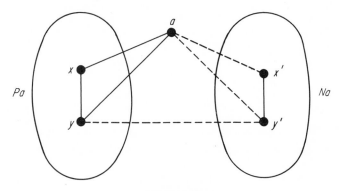

Figure 3.5

So in the set $X_1 = Pa \cup \{a\}$, all the edges are positive; and they are so in the set $X_2 = Na$; and all the edges are negative between X_1 and X_2.

The division X_1, X_2 constitutes a bipartition of X; indeed $X_1 \cap X_2 = \emptyset$ since, because an edge cannot be simultaneously positive and negative, we have $Pa \cap Na = \emptyset$, and $a \notin Na$; and $X_1 \cup X_2 = X$ since, G being complete, any point of X belongs to Pa or to Na, or is point a itself.

Note finally that this bipartition does not depend at all on point a chosen for the demonstration; indeed, given a point $b \neq a$, if $b \in Pa$, we have

$$Pb \cup \{b\} = Pa \cup \{a\} = X_1,$$

and

$$Nb = Na = X_2;$$

if $b \in Na$, we have $Pb \cup \{b\} = Na = X_2,$

and

$$Nb = Pa \cup \{a\} = X_1.$$

Proof of sufficiency. Let X_1 and X_2 be a bipartition of X satisfying the condition. Given a triangle (abc); if these three points all belong to X_1 or all to X_2, the three edges are positive; if we put, for example $a \in X_1$ and b and $c \in X_2$, the edges (ab) and (ac) are negative and edge (bc) is positive; in both cases, the triangle is balanced.

THEOREM 3.2.   *Definitions D_4 and D_5 are equivalent.*

Proof. $D_5 \Rightarrow D_4$, since if, by D_5, all the cycles are positive, the triangles in particular are positive and, by D_3, in a state of balance; hence D_4.

$D_4 \Rightarrow D_5$. Indeed, if D_4 is met by a graph, X is partitioned into X_1 and X_2 as introduced by Theorem 3.1. Given a cycle of an arbitrary length. If all its points belong to X_1, or all to X_2, all its edges are positive; if that cycle has points in X_1 and the others in X_2, each time we pass from X_1 to X_2, we have a negative edge, and another negative edge by returning from X_2 to X_1. Therefore, the number of negative edges of the cycle is an even number; in both cases, the cycle is positive and D_5 is satisfied (Fig. 3.6).

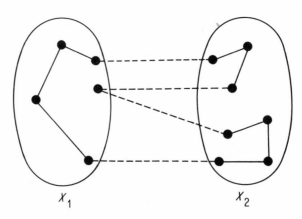

Figure 3.6

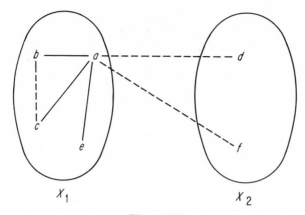

Figure 3.7

Theorem 3.1 provides, by its demonstration, a practical means to judge of the balance of a graph: we choose an arbitrary point a, and put $X_1 = Pa \cup \{a\}$ and $X_2 = Na$, which is very quick, and we easily verify whether these sets have the properties defined by the theorem. Thus, it can be seen immediately that the graph of Fig. 3.3 is not balanced, since b and $c \in Pa$ and $(bc) \in N$ (Fig. 3.7).

But the real interest of the theorem is in the proposition that any social situation having something more than two antagonistic "blocks" is an unbalanced situation (recall that one of the "blocks" can be empty: a situation of universal agreement, which is balanced).

We shall come back to this point in the last paragraph of this chapter.

The interest of Theorem 3.2 is more technical: it shows that in *complete* algebraic graphs, balance properties can be defined only at the very simple level of the triangle, without the necessity of considering cycles of any length. This observation will lead us to results unnoticed by various authors who always consider all the cycles.

THEOREM 3.3. *The product of the signs of the four triangles constructed on four points is always positive.*

Proof. Let a, b, c, d be four points; the four triangles constructed on these points are (abc), (abd), (acd) and (bcd). Put

$$S = s(abc) \times s(abd) \times s(acd) \times s(bcd).$$

According to D_2, we have

$$S = [s(ab) \times s(ac) \times s(bc)] \times [s(ab) \times s(ad) \times s(bd)]$$
$$\times [s(ac) \times s(ad) \times s(cd)] \times [s(bc) \times s(bd) \times s(cd)];$$

The product of the signs being associative and commutative, it becomes

$$S = [s(ab) \times s(ab)] \times [s(ac) \times s(ac)] \times [s(ad) \times s(ad)]$$
$$\times [s(bc) \times s(bc)] \times [s(bd) \times s(bd)] \times [s(cd) \times s(cd)].$$

So, whatever the sign of each edge, each bracket is positive, and S is always positive.

(D_6) The *balance base with axis a* of a complete algebraic graph G consists of the list of the signs of the triangles containing a.

A graph of n points has n balance bases, each having for axis a different point. For example, here are the balance bases with axes a and d of the graph in Fig. 3.3.

$$a: \begin{cases} s(abc) = (-); & s(abd) = (-); & s(abe) = (+); & s(abf) = (+); \\ s(acd) = (+); & s(ace) = (+); & s(acf) = (+); \\ s(ade) = (+); & s(adf) = (+); & s(aef) = (-); \end{cases}$$

$$d: \begin{cases} s(dab) = (-); & s(dac) = (+); & s(dae) = (+); & s(daf) = (+); \\ s(dbc) = (+); & s(dbe) = (-); & s(dbf) = (-); \\ s(dce) = (+); & s(dcf) = (+); & s(def) = (-). \end{cases}$$

Note that the base of axis a contains three negative triangles, while the base of axis d contains four such triangles.

THEOREM 3.4. *If a balance base of a complete algebraic graph G is known, the signs of all the triangles of G are deduced from it.*

Proof. Given a base with axis a. What is the sign of triangle (bcd), which is not given by the base? Consider the four triangles constructed on the four points a, b, c, and d. Let

$$S' = s(abc) \times s(abd) \times s(acd);$$

S' is known from the base with axis a. Let S be defined as in Theorem 3.3; we then have

$$S = S' \times s(bcd);$$

Since, from Theorem 3.3, S is always positive, it follows that

$$s(bcd) = S'$$

Theorems 3.3 and 3.4 introduce in fact what can be called the notion of *degrees of freedom* into the study of the balance of a graph. Let us deal with the four points a, b, c, d (Theorem 3.3).

Suppose that, on these four points, one wishes to construct a graph by freely choosing the sign of the greatest possible number of triangles. Theorem 3.3 says that the sign of only three triangles can be freely chosen. Note moreover that this choice of the sign of the triangles is, to a certain degree, independent of the sign of the edges. On four points, any three triangles always have one point in common; if one wishes to choose $s(abc)$, $s(abd)$, and $s(acd)$, one considers edges (ab), (ac), and (ad), which can have any sign—for example, as in Fig. 3.8. One sets $s(abc) = (+)$; $s(abd) = (+)$; and $s(acd) = (-)$; in order to obtain this result, the appropriate signs are assigned to the edges

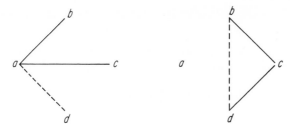

Figure 3.8

(*bc*), (*bd*), and (*cd*) (Fig. 3.8); but in so doing, the sign of triangle (*bcd*) is determined.

The notion of balance base and Theorem 3.4 generalize this argument to any *n*. Let $X' = X - \{a\}$, *a* being the axis of the base considered; we have $|X'| = (n - 1)$. All edges not including *a* are defined on the basis of X'; their number is $(n - 1)(n - 2)/2$; the triangles of the base all consist of two points of X' and of *a*, and any edge not including *a* and joined with *a* defines a triangle of the base. There are then $(n - 1)(n - 2)/2$ triangles in a base of an *n*-point graph; this number measures the degrees of freedom of the graph.

THEOREM 3.5. *A complete algebraic graph is balanced if and only if all the triangles of a base are positive.*

Proof. If all the triangles of a base are positive, all the triangles of the graph are positive (and, by definition, the graph is balanced). Indeed, for any triangle (*bcd*) not appearing in the base with axis *a*, we have (cf. demonstration of Theorem 3.4):

$$s(bcd) = s(abc) \times s(abd) \times s(acd) = (+)$$

On the other hand, if the graph is balanced, all these triangles are positive (by definition) and in particular those of a base.

THEOREM 3.6. *All the triangles of a complete algebraic graph are unbalanced if and only if all the triangles of a base are negative.*

Proof. The proof is parallel to that of the preceding theorem, and the equation appearing there becomes

$$s(bcd) = s(abc) \times s(abd) \times s(acd) = (-).$$

THEOREM 3.7. *The number of balanced complete algebraic graphs of n points is* $2^{(n-1)}$.

Proof. This results directly from Theorem 3.5 and from the considerations developed in relation to Theorems 3.3 and 3.4. In a graph of *n* points, there are $(n - 1)$ edges containing *a*; each of these edges has two possibilities: positive or negative; hence, in all, $2^{(n-1)}$ possibilities. Starting from each of these possibilities, a base with axis *a* can be constructed, of which all the triangles are positive.

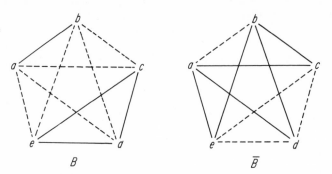

Figure 3.9

From Theorem 3.5, it follows that all the balanced complete algebraic graphs of n points have identical bases.

Theorem 3.6 introduces a particular type of unbalanced graph: the graph all the triangles of which are negative. Let B be a balanced graph, and $\bar{B}$ a graph all the triangles of which are negative, which will be called an *anti-balanced* graph. For a given n, there exists a biunique correspondence between set $\{B\}$ of the $2^{(n-1)}$ balanced graphs, and set $\{\bar{B}\}$ of the antibalanced graphs. Note first that Theorem 3.7 can be carried over to the antibalanced graphs, and shows that

$$|\{\bar{B}\}| = |\{B\}| = 2^{(n-1)}.$$

If a triangle is positive, and if the sign of each edge is changed, it becomes negative. Indeed, a positive triangle has one or three positive edges; by changing the sign of the edges, a triangle with one or three negative edges is obtained.

Then if $B = (X; P, N)$ is a balanced graph, graph $\bar{B} = (X; \bar{P}, \bar{N})$, which is deduced from it by changing the sign of all the edges of B, is an antibalanced graph. We have: $\bar{P} = N$, and $\bar{N} = P$. Graphs B and $\bar{B}$ in Fig. 3.9 are constructed according to this principle.

4. Degree of Unbalance of a Graph

We have studied balanced graphs, and said a few words on antibalanced graphs. But what can be said about any complete algebraic graph? The psycho-social situations represented by any two graphs, no doubt, are not always equally unpleasant to those who are in them: graphs must be classified according to a *degree of unbalance*.

Cartwright and Harary (1956) suggest the following definition, which applies also to incomplete graphs:

If $c(G)$ is the number of cycles of G; $c_+(G)$, the number of positive cycles of G; and $b(G)$, the degree of balance, then

$$b(G) = \frac{c_+ G}{c G}.$$

This index varies from zero to unity; it is a balance index. The unbalance index could be $1 - b(G)$.

This index can be criticized for giving the same weight to all cycles, whatever their length. A weight increase to the length of the cycle could be imagined— for example, if m is the length of a cycle, define a *decreasing* function $f(m)$, and put

$$c_+^{(m)}(G) = \text{the number of positive cycles of length } m \text{ of } G,$$

$$c^{(m)}(G) = \text{the number of cycles of length } m \text{ of } G,$$

and

$$b(G) = \sum_m f(m) \frac{c_+^{(m)}(G)}{c^{(m)}(G)}.$$

If we concentrated on the triangles ($m = 3$) we could put

$$f(m) = \begin{cases} 1 & \text{if } m = 3, \\ 0 & \text{if } m > 3; \end{cases}$$

hence

$$b(G) = \frac{c_+^{(3)}(G)}{c^{(3)}(G)}.$$

Nevertheless, consider graphs G_1 and G_2 in Fig. 3.10. The first one has six negative triangles out of ten,

$$(abc), (ade), (bcd), (bce), (bde), \text{ and } (cde),$$

while the second one has only four:

$$(abc), (abd), (bce), \text{ and } (bde);$$

therefore $b(G_1) < b(G_2)$, if the last definition of $b(G)$ is utilized.

Nonetheless, it is sufficient to change the sign of two edges of G_1: (bc) and (de), and equally of two edges of G_2: (bc) and (bd), in order to get balanced graph B in Fig. 3.10.

This leads us to define the degree of unbalance of a graph:

(D_7) *The degree of unbalance* $\delta(G)$ *of an algebraic graph* G *is measured by*

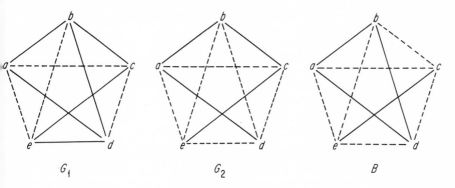

G_1 G_2 B

Figure 3.10

the power of the smallest set of edges of G whose sign change produces a balanced graph.

This is the definition given by Abelson and Rosenberg (1958). This type of definition is frequent in the theory of graphs: Luce (1953) uses it for the degree of connectivity of a graph; we have utilized it for the degree of intransitivity of a graph (Flament, 1958d).

Abelson and Rosenberg (1958) give a technique to find the degree of unbalance of a graph G which, in its essence, boils down rigorously to this: if G has n points, draw the list of the $2^{(n-1)}$ balanced graphs of $\{B\}$ and compare G to each element of $\{B\}$; for each comparison, note the number of edges not having the same sign in G and in B; the degree of unbalance is the smallest number noted.

Starting from the notion of the balance base of a graph G, we want to suggest a method which

1. gives the degree of unbalance $\delta(G)$;
2. gives all the sets of the edges of G, of power $\delta(G)$, such that the sign change of all the edges of a set leads to a balanced graph.

Let us establish a mapping between the set of the $(n-1)(n-2)/2$ triangles of the balance base with axis a of G, and the set V of the $n(n-1)/2$ edges of G; in the table of the Cartesian product of these two sets, we will hatch the cells corresponding to an edge and a triangle, if and only if the edge does *not* belong to the triangle:

	(ab)	(ac)	(ad)	(bc)	(bd)	(cd)
(abc)			▨		▨	▨
(abd)		▨		▨		▨
(acd)	▨			▨	▨	

We will distinguish in V two parts: Va, the set of edges containing axis a, and $\bar{V}a$, the set of edges not containing a. Such a table presents remarkable regularities:

1. In each row, there are three blank cells, since a triangle has three edges;
2. In each column of Va, there are $(n-2)$ blank cells, since each edge containing a—for example, (ab)—forms a triangle of the base with each of the other points of $X - \{a, b\}$, of which there are $(n-2)$.
3. In each column of $\bar{V}a$, there is one blank cell, since an edge not containing a forms, with a, only one triangle of the base.
4. For any two columns of Va, there exists one and only one row where the cells corresponding to the two columns are blank, and this row has no other blank cell in Va, since two edges containing a—for example, (ab) and (ac)—determine only one triangle of the base: (abc).

In all the blank cells of a row, we will put a (+) if the corresponding triangle is positive, or a (−) if the corresponding triangle is negative. The table thus made is called *structure of the balance base with axis a of G.*

Thus, the graph of Fig. 3.11 has for base structure with axis a the following table:

	(ab)	(ac)	(ad)	(ae)	(bc)	(bd)	(be)	(cd)	(ce)	(de)
(abc)	−	−			−					
(abd)	+		+			+				
(abe)	+			+			+			
(acd)		−	−					−		
(ace)		−		−					−	
(ade)			−	−						−

(In order to simplify the table, the hatchings have been omitted; they are useless when the nonhatched cells are marked with + or −.)

If we change the sign of an edge, the sign of the triangles of the base containing this edge changes also. For example, in the preceding structure, if I change the sign of (ab), I will have to put (+)'s in the place of (−)'s in row (abc), and (−)'s in the place of (+)'s in rows (abd) and (abe). Through a series of operations of this type, it is possible to make all signs positive; then the resulting graph is balanced.

(D_8) We call *balancing set of G* any set of edges of G of which the changing of the sign gives a balanced graph.

To any graph G of n points, we can associate $2^{(n-1)}$ distinct balancing sets, each giving one of the $2^{(n-1)}$ balanced graphs; if we designate these sets by $\mathcal{E}_i(G)$, $i = 1, 2, \ldots, 2^{(n-1)}$, definition D_7 of the degree of unbalance can be reformulated:

$$(D'_7) \qquad \delta(G) = \min_i \{ \mid \mathcal{E}_i(G) \mid \}.$$

A balancing set of G whose power is the degree of unbalance $\delta(G)$, is called a *minimum balancing set of G.*

Theorem 3.8 allows the construction of balancing sets, not necessarily minimums, of G starting from the structure of a base of G.

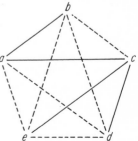

Figure 3.11

THEOREM 3.8. *Given the structure of the base with axis a of a graph* G; $V'a$ *a subset of set* Va *of the edges containing* a; $X'a$ *the subset of the points of* X *constituting with* a *the edges of* $V'a$,

$$X'a = \{x \mid x \in X, (ax) \in V'a\},$$

we construct a set $\bar{V}'a$ *of edges not containing* a *by putting* $(xy) \in \bar{V}'a$ *if*

$$s(axy) = (+) \quad and \quad x \in X'a, \ y \notin X'a$$

or if $\qquad s(axy) = (-) \quad and \quad x \ and \ y \in X'a \quad or \quad x \ and \ y \notin X'a.$

$\mathcal{E} = (V'a \cup \bar{V}'a)$ *is a balancing set of* G.

Proof. Suppose that $s(axy) = (+)$. If $x \in X'a$ and $y \notin X'a$, we have $(ax) \in V'a$ and $(ay) \notin V'a$; in that case $(xy) \in V'a$. Therefore, by changing the sign of the edges of $\mathcal{E}$, only two of the edges of (axy) are changed: (ax) and (xy), and the sign of (axy) is not changed: it remains positive.

Suppose that $s(axy) = (-)$. If x and $y \in X'a$, the three edges of the triangle shall be changed, the triangle becoming positive; if x and $y \notin X'a$, only the sign of edge (xy) shall be changed, the triangle becoming positive.

This theorem tells us that, to a certain degree, we will have to be concerned only with sign changes of edges containing a.

Example. In order to obtain a balanced graph from the graph in Fig. 3.11, we decide to change, among the edges containing a, only edges (ab) and (bc):

$$V'a = \{(ab), (ac)\} \quad and \quad X'a = \{b, c\}.$$

Consider successively the edges not containing a:

(bc): $s(abc) = (-)$ and b and $c \in X'a$; therefore $(bc) \in \bar{V}'a$;

(bd): $s(abd) = (+)$ and $b \in X'a$, $d \notin X'a$; therefore $(bd) \in \bar{V}'a$;

(be): $s(abe) = (+)$ and $b \in X'a$, $e \notin X'a$; therefore $(be) \in \bar{V}'a$;

(cd): $s(acd) = (-)$ and $c \in X'a$, $d \notin X'a$; therefore $(cd) \notin \bar{V}'a$;

(ce): $s(ace) = (-)$ and $c \in X'a$, $e \notin X'a$; therefore $(ce) \notin \bar{V}'a$;

(de): $s(ade) = (-)$ and d and $e \notin X'a$; therefore $(de) \in \bar{V}'a$.

We therefore have

$$\bar{V}'a = \{(bc), (bd), (be), (de)\}$$

and $\quad \mathcal{E} = \{(ab), (ac), (bc), (bd), (be), (de)\};$

by changing the sign of these edges in the graph in Fig. 3.11, the graph in Fig. 3.12 is obtained, which is balanced.

Let us define, for any x, $y \in X$, x and y being distinct from axis a:

$$\delta(x) = \text{the number of negative triangles} \text{ containing edge } (ax);$$

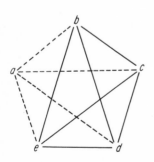

Figure 3.12

$$\delta(xy) = \begin{cases} 0 & \text{if } s(axy) = (+), \\ 1 & \text{if } s(axy) = (-). \end{cases}$$

THEOREM 3.9. *If the base with axis a of G includes K_a negative triangles, and we put a set $V'a$, we have*

$$|\mathcal{E}| = K_a + |X'_a|(n - |X'_a|) - 2 \sum_{x \in X'a} \delta(x) + 4 \sum_{x, y \in X'a} \delta(xy).$$

Proof. By changing $(ax) \in V'a$, we change the sign of the $(n - 2)$ triangles to which belongs (ax); therefore, by changing all the edges of $V'a$, we bring about a number of sign changes of triangles equal to $|X'a|(n - 2)$; but if (ax) and $(ay) \in V'a$, triangle (axy) has had *two* sign changes, and all in all, $s(axy)$ remains unchanged. There are $|X'a|(|X'a| - 1)/2$ triangles having thus two sign changes canceling each other; each of the other sign changes modifies the sign of a triangle; we therefore have m modified triangles:

$$m = [\,|X'a|(n - 2)\,] - [\,|X'a|(|X'a| - 1)\,]$$
$$= |X'a|(n - |X'a| - 1).$$

These m changes can be from negative to positive, or vice versa. The number of changes from negative to positive is

$$h = \sum_{x \in X'a} \delta(x) - 2 \sum_{x, y \in X'a} \delta(xy);$$

indeed, by changing $(ax) \in V'a$, $\delta(x)$ negative triangles become positive; by changing $(ay) \in V'a$, $\delta(y)$ negative triangles become positive; but if $s(axy) = (-)$, this sign remains negative when (ax) and (ay) are both changed at the same time. By changing (ax) and (ay), we have therefore made positive $[\delta(x) + \delta(y) - 2\delta(xy)]$ negative triangles, since $\delta(xy) = 1$ if and only if $s(axy) = (-)$ and since triangle (axy) is counted twice in $[\delta(x) + \delta(y)]$; by generalizing, the announced value of h is found.

Since m triangles have had their signs modified, and since h triangles have passed from negative to positive, there are $k = m - h$ of them which have passed from negative to positive.

Since we had K_a negative triangles, we now have K'_a negative triangles:

$$K'_a = K_a - h + k = K_a - 2h + m.$$

If triangle $(ax'y')$ is among these K'_a negative triangles, it can be made positive only by changing $(x'y')$, since all the edges containing a which we wanted to change have already been changed. Therefore, there will be K'_a changes of edges not containing a. As there are already $|X'a|$ changes of edges containing a, the total number of changes will be

$$|\mathcal{E}| = |X'a| + K'_a = |X'a| + K_a - 2h + m;$$

hence the theorem, by replacing h and m by their values.

From this theorem results an algorithm allowing us to find all at once all the minimum balancing sets of a graph, which gives the degree of the unbalance of the graph. It is sufficient to calculate the value of $|\mathcal{E}|$ for all the possible sets $V'a$, by proceeding with the smallest sets.

Example. Given the graph in Fig. 3.13, whose base structure with axis *a* is the following:

	(ab)	(ac)	(ad)	(ae)	(bc)	(bd)	(be)	(cd)	(ce)	(de)
(abc)	−	−			−					
(abd)	+		+			+				
(abe)	+			+			+			
(acd)		−	−					−		
(ace)		+		+					+	
(ade)			−	−						−

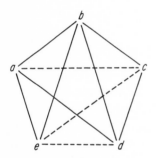

Figure 3.13

We have
$$\delta(b) = 1; \quad \delta(c) = 2; \quad \delta(d) = 2; \quad \delta(e) = 1;$$
and
$$\delta(bc) = 1; \quad \delta(bd) = 0; \quad \delta(be) = 0;$$
$$\delta(cd) = 1; \quad \delta(ce) = 0; \quad \delta(de) = 1.$$

K_a is equal to 3: Let $|V'a| = 0$; in this case $|\mathcal{E}| = K_a = 3$. Let $|V'a| = 1$; there are $(n-1) = 4$ possibilities:

$$V'a = \{(ab)\} \text{ or } \{(ac)\} \text{ or } \{(ad)\} \text{ or } \{(ae)\};$$

In all cases, we have
$$K_a + |X'a|(n - |X'a|) = 7;$$

for $V'a = \{(ab)\}$, we have $-2\,\delta(b) = -2$, and, since $\delta(xy)$ need not be considered, we obtain

$$|\mathcal{E}| = 5;$$

and so on. The research can be presented in a table such as the following (on opposite page).

It is useless to consider sets of greater power; indeed, since $V'a \subset \mathcal{E}$, we have $|\mathcal{E}| \geq |V'a|$; if a set $|V'a| > 3$ is considered, we would therefore have $|\mathcal{E}| > 3$; but we already have sets with $|\mathcal{E}| = 3$. We conclude that

$$\delta(G) = 3.$$

The sets $V'a$ leading to $|\mathcal{E}| = 3$ are

$$\emptyset; \quad \{(ac)\}; \quad \{(ad)\}; \quad \{(ab); (ad)\}; \quad \{(ac), (ae)\};$$

$\|V'a\|$ $= \|X'a\|$	$\|X'a\|(n-\|X'a\|)$ $+ Ka$	$V'a$	$-2 \sum\limits_{x\in X'a} \delta(x)$ $+4 \sum\limits_{x,y\in X'a} \delta(xy)$	$\|\mathcal{E}\|$
0	3	$\emptyset$	0	$\underline{3}$
1	7	(ab) (ac) (ad) (ae)	-2 -4 -4 -2	5 $\underline{3}$ $\underline{3}$ 5
2	9	$(ab),\ (ac)$ $(ab),\ (ad)$ $(ab),\ (ae)$ $(ac),\ (ad)$ $(ac),\ (ae)$ $(ad),\ (ae)$	-2 -6 -4 -4 -6 -2	7 $\underline{3}$ $\underline{5}$ 5 $\underline{3}$ 7
3	9	$(ab),\ (ac),\ (ad)$ $(ab),\ (ac),\ (ae)$ $(ab),\ (ad),\ (ae)$ $(ac),\ (ad),\ (ae)$	-2 -4 -4 -2	7 5 5 7

the corresponding sets $\mathcal{E}$ are, through Theorem 3.8,

$$\{(bc), (cd), (de)\}; \qquad \{(ac), (ce), (de)\}; \qquad \{(ad), (be), (bd)\};$$

$$\{(ab), (ad), (be)\}; \qquad \{(ac), (ae), (be)\}.$$

Each of the five sets designates the edges whose sign it is sufficient to change in order that the graph be balanced. They are the only sets of power 3 which give this result (evidently we find the same sets by starting from a base with any axis).

Figure 3.14 gives, by way of example, the graphs obtained by starting from Fig. 3.13, by changing

$$\{(bc), (ce), (de)\} \quad \text{or} \quad \{(ac), (ae), (be)\}.$$

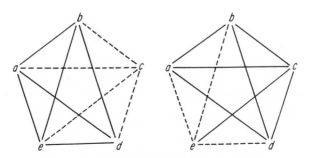

Figure 3.14

THEOREM 3.10. *If $\bar{B}$ is an antibalanced complete algebraic graph (all its triangles being negative), then*

$$\delta(\bar{B}) = \frac{n(n-2) + \varepsilon}{4},$$

where
$$\varepsilon = \begin{cases} 1 & \text{if } n \text{ is an odd number,} \\ 0 & \text{if } n \text{ is an even number,} \end{cases}$$

and for any $a \in X$, any set $V'a$ of power

$$|V'a| = \frac{(n-2) \pm \varepsilon}{2}$$

leads to a minimum set of balancing.

Proof. If $\bar{B}$'s triangles are all negative, we always have whatever axis a of the base, and set Xa considered

$$Ka = \frac{(n-1)(n-2)}{2},$$

$$\sum_{x \in X'_a} \delta(x) = |X'_a|(n-2),$$

$$\sum_{x,y \in X'_a} \delta(xy) = \frac{|X'a|(|X'a| - 1)}{2},$$

since for any x and y

$$\delta(x) = \delta(y) = (n-2) \quad \text{and} \quad \delta(xy) = 1.$$

By replacing these values in the formula of Theorem 3.9, we obtain

$$|\mathcal{E}| = \frac{(n-1)(n-2)}{2} + |X'a|(n-|X'a|) - 2|X'a|(n-2) + 2|X'a|(|X'a| - 1)$$

$$= \frac{(n-1)(n-2)}{2} + |X'a|(|X'a| - n + 2).$$

Minimize this expression relative to $|X'a|$: derived from

$$|\mathcal{E}| = 2|X'a|_{\min} - (n-2) = 0;$$

hence

$$|X'a|_{\min} = \frac{(n-2)}{2}$$

$|X'a|$ having to be a whole number, the correction ε intervenes, and we have

$$|X'a|_{\min} = \frac{(n-2) \pm \varepsilon}{2}.$$

By replacing this value in the expression of $|\mathcal{E}|$ we find

$$|\mathcal{E}|_{\min} = \delta(\bar{B}) = \frac{n(n-2) + \varepsilon}{4}.$$

We may think that the antibalanced graphs are the most unbalanced graphs of all, therefore let us propose the following conjecture:

Conjecture. If G is a complete algebraic graph of n points, its unbalance degree is

$$\delta(G) \leqq \frac{n(n - 2) + \varepsilon}{4}, \qquad \varepsilon = \begin{cases} 1 & \text{if } n \text{ is odd,} \\ 0 & \text{if } n \text{ is even.} \end{cases}$$

Abelson and Rosenberg (1958) give this conjecture as a theorem; unfortunately, they give no demonstration of it, and we have been unable, up to now, to retrace it.

Intuition suggests the following argument:

Let $\bar{B}$ be an antibalanced graph, and $\mathcal{E}(\bar{B})$ a minimum balancing set of $\bar{B}$. By changing successively the sign of the edges of $\mathcal{E}(\bar{B})$ in a given order, we construct a series of graphs less and less balanced; by considering all the possible $\bar{B}$'s and, for each one, all the possible $\mathcal{E}(\bar{B})$'s in all possible orders, we must construct all the graphs possible. This argument is false; indeed, if it were true, it would imply that for any G there exists a minimum set $\mathcal{E}(G)$ included in one of the minimum sets $\mathcal{E}(\bar{B})$; but the graph in Fig. 3.13 is a counterexample.

Through Theorem 3.10, we construct the minimum balancing sets for a graph $\bar{B}$ of $n = 5$ points; we find

$$| V'a | = \frac{(n - 2) \pm \varepsilon}{2} = 1 \text{ or } 2;$$

hence the sets $V'a$:

$$\{(ab)\}; \ \{(ac)\}; \ \{(ad)\}; \ \{(ae)\};$$
$$\{(ab), (ac)\}; \ \{(ab), (ad)\}; \ \{(ab), (ae)\};$$
$$\{(ac), (ad)\}; \ \{(ac), (ae)\}; \ \{(ad), (ae)\};$$

and, through Theorem 3.8, the sets $\mathcal{E}(\bar{B})$:

$$\{(ab), (cd), (ce), (de)\}; \ \{(ac), (bd), (be), (de)\};$$
$$\{(ad), (bc), (be), (ce)\}; \ \{(ae), (bc), (bd), (cd)\};$$
$$\{(ab), (ac), (bc), (de)\}; \ \{(ab), (ad), (bd), (ce)\};$$
$$\{(ab), (ae), (be), (cd)\}; \ \{(ac), (ad), (be), (cd)\};$$
$$\{(ac), (ae), (bd), (ae)\}; \ \{(ad), (ae), (bc), (de)\}.$$

By comparing this list with that established in relation to the graph in Fig. 3.13, we see that there is not one inclusion relation; with this example we lose hope of proving the conjecture through the argument suggested, but we notice that it does not invalidate the conjecture.

5. Balancing Process

The very notions of balance and unbalance imply that one goes from unbalance to balance. A group whose structure is represented by an unbalanced algebraic graph will modify its structure until it is in a state of balance. But by which processes? According to which laws? We will state a first hypothesis.

(H_1) The balancing of an algebraic graph is done through a series of operations each of which includes changing the sign of one and only one edge.

This hypothesis does not imply that the group decides to change an edge, then examines the new situation and starts over again. We think only that the state of unbalance of the group creates tensions in the whole structure, which demand the change of many edges, but that it is quite probable that one edge will give in before the others, by chance; then a new situation is created, some new tensions manifest themselves, and the process starts over again.

This hypothesis leads to the balancing process being made through a route in the lattice $\mathscr{L}_n^\sigma$ of the symmetric graphs of n points. This lattice, which we have defined for nonalgebraic graphs (cf. Chap. 1, Sec. 8.4), can be used for complete algebraic graphs. Indeed, in a complete algebraic graph all the possible edges, of number $n(n - 1)/2$, are present, but distributed into two classes:

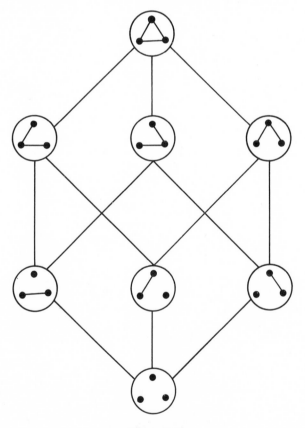

Figure 3.15

set P of the positive edges and set N of the negative edges. Knowing n, we know set V of all the edges, that is to say, $V = (P \cup N)$; and the graph is entirely defined if P only is known. N is deducted from it by complementarity: $N = V - P$. If an edge is not in the list P of the positive edges, which is given, it means that it is in the list N, not given, of the negative edges. Therefore, for each ordinary nonoriented graph $G^* = (X; P)$ a unique complete algebraic graph can be made to correspond: $G = (X; P, N = V - P)$, and conversely.

If $n = 3$, and $X = \{a, b, c\}$, we have $V = \{(ab), (ac), (bc)\}$, and all the ordinary graphs that can be constructed on X are the following:

$$G^* = (X; P)$$

with P: 　　　　　　$\emptyset$; $\{(ab)\}$; $\{(ac)\}$; $\{(bc)\}$;

$$\{(ab), (ac)\}; \ \{(ab), (bc)\}; \ \{(ac), (bc)\};$$

$$\{(ab), (ac), (bc)\}.$$

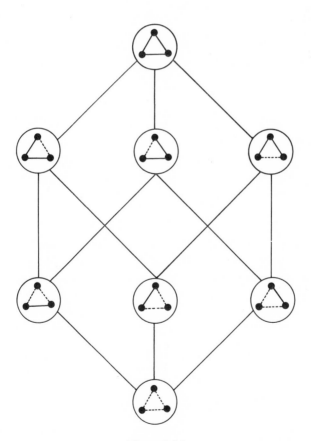

Figure 3.16

Lattice $\mathscr{L}_n^\sigma$ of these eight possible graphs is given by Fig. 3.15.

If to each $G^* = (X; P)$ is made to correspond the complete algebraic graph $G = (X; P, N = V - P)$, the lattice of Fig. 3.16 is obtained. It is in this last lattice that the balancing process will be capable of being described as a route from one graph to another.

THEOREM 3.11. *If G is a complete algebraic graph of n points, the unbalance degree $\delta(G)$ is the length of the shortest of the paths going in $\mathscr{L}_n^\sigma$ of G to the balanced graphs.*

Proof. This theorem is in fact a quite evident reformulation of the definition of $\delta(G)$ (D_7 or D_7'). In the lattice of the ordinary graphs (cf. Fig. 3.15), two graphs $G_i^* = (X, P_i)$ and $G_j^* = (X; P_j)$ are joined by a line if and only if the symmetric difference $(P_j \oplus P_j)$ has one element only (cf. Theorem 1.5), that is, if we pass from one to the other by adding or subtracting one and only one edge. If we pass from G_i^* and G_j^* to the corresponding complete algebraic graphs G_i and G_j, to add an edge is the same as making positive a negative edge, and to subtract an edge, the same as making negative a positive edge (cf. Fig. 3.16). Therefore, the length of a path in $\mathscr{L}_n^\sigma$ between two complete algebraic graphs corresponds to a number of edges whose sign is changed in order to pass from one graph to the other.

We will say that two graphs are *adjacent* (in $\mathscr{L}_n^\sigma$) if and only if they differ in the sign of one and only one edge, that is, if and only if one *covers* the other.

Hypothesis H_1 is equivalent to saying that a graph becomes an adjacent graph. But a graph of n points has $n(n-1)/2$ adjacent graphs, since it has $n(n-1)/2$ edges each one of which can change sign. What are the adjacent graphs into which the graph will be transformable?

We can imagine that the group of graph G gives itself as a goal a state of precise balance of graph B and that it will choose, among the adjacents of G, the graphs appearing on the tracks $\theta(GB)$ of $\mathscr{L}_n^\sigma$; but this implies that, one way or another, the group has at each moment a knowledge of $\mathscr{L}_n^\sigma$, which is hardly admissible. A hypothesis must be adopted which allows the inclusion of local possibilities only. For example:

(H_2) A graph will be transformed into one of the least unbalanced graphs of the set including the graph itself and its adjacents.

According to the unbalance measure adopted, the results will be quite different. Note that certain unbalance indices can be such that an unbalanced graph would have as adjacents only graphs less balanced than itself. In this case the graph will never attain a state of balance, unless supplementary hypotheses are introduced.

We will adopt here as a measure of unbalance the degree of unbalance $\delta(G)$ already studied above (Sec. 4):

(H_3) The levels of unbalance referred to in H_2 are measured by the degree of unbalance δ defined in D_7.

THEOREM 3.12. *If G and G' are adjacent complete algebraic graphs, $\delta(G) - \delta(G') = -1, 0,$ or $+1$.*

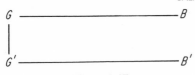

Figure 3.17

Proof. Let B and B' be two balanced graphs, such that the distances $d(GB)$ and $d(G'B')$ in $\mathscr{L}_n^\sigma$ are $d(GB) = \delta(G)$ and $d(G'B') = \delta(G)$ (Fig. 3.17). Consider the path consisting of the edge (GG') and a track $\theta(G'B')$; it leads from G to a balanced graph, and its length, which is equal to $[\delta(G') + 1]$ cannot therefore be inferior to $\delta(G)$ (cf. Theorem 3.11):

$$\delta(G') + 1 \geqq \delta(G),$$

hence
$$\delta(G) - \delta(G') \leqq + 1.$$

By considering in the same manner the path formed by the edge $(G'G)$ and a track $\theta(GB)$, we find

$$\delta(G) - \delta(G') \geqq - 1,$$

hence the theorem.

That adjacent graphs do *not* necessarily differ in their degrees of unbalance is attested by the example of Fig. 3.18: the two graphs of degree $\delta = 1$ are adjacent indeed, since it is sufficient to change the sign of edge (dc) in order

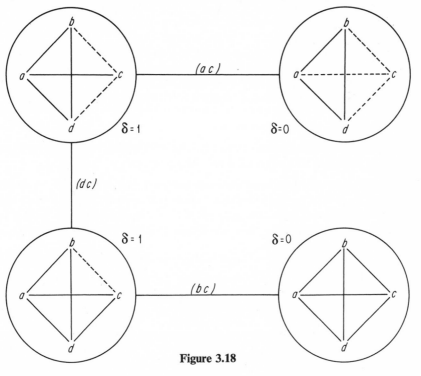

Figure 3.18

to pass from one to the other; and they are indeed both of degree $\delta = 1$ since it is sufficient to change the sign of only one edge, (ac) or (bc) depending on the case, in order to obtain graphs for which it is easy to verify that they are of degree $\delta = 0$, that is, balanced.

THEOREM 3.13. *A complete algebraic graph G has no adjacent G′ such that* $\delta(G) - \delta(G') = 1$ *if and only if G is balanced.*

Proof. Let G be an unbalanced graph, and B a balanced graph such that $d(GB) = \delta(G)$; there exists in $\mathscr{L}_n^a$ a track $\theta(GB)$; let G' be a point of this track, adjacent to G. We have, of course,

$$\delta(G') = \delta(G) - 1.$$

If G is a balanced graph, we then have $\delta(G) = 0$; in order that $\delta(G) - \delta(G') = 1$, we would need to have $\delta(G') = -1$, which is impossible by definition of δ.

These theorems assure us that if the balancing process follows hypotheses H_1 to H_3, it will have a satisfactory ending: we will end up with a balanced

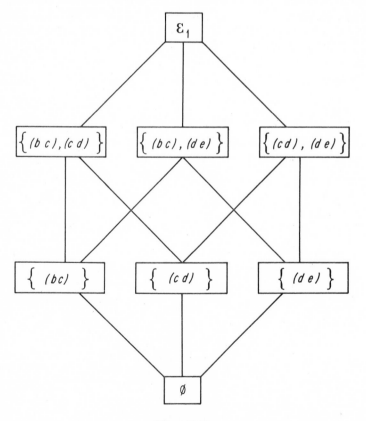

Figure 3.19

graph, since at each stage of the process we will be able to pass to a more balanced adjacent graph. Moreover, it is clear that if we start from a graph G, the process will have a number of stages equal to $\delta(G)$, since at each stage the unbalance is reduced by one unit.

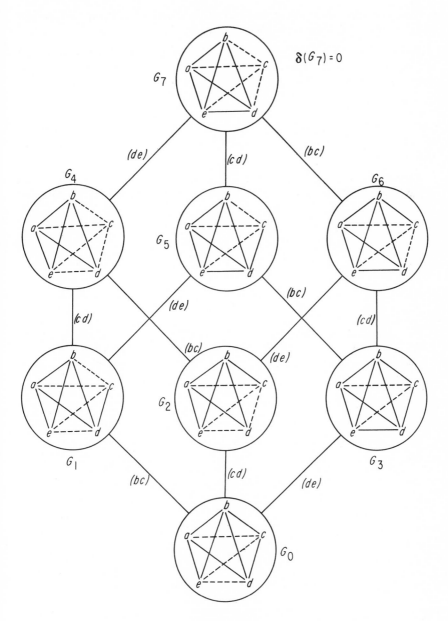

Figure 3.20

In general, a graph G can lead to many balanced graphs. Indeed, we have seen that a graph could admit of many minimum sets of balancing.

Hypotheses H_1 and H_3 must therefore be completed with a hypothesis defining the process:

(H_4) If G has k adjacent graphs more balanced than itself, the probability of passing from G to each of these k graphs is $1/k$.

The balancing process is therefore brought down to *random walk* on *certain paths of* $\mathscr{L}_n^\sigma$. In order to make these paths more precise, consider one of the minimum balancing sets. For instance, for the graph in Fig. 3.13, consider

$$\mathcal{E}_1 = \{(bc), (cd), (de)\}.$$

Let $p(\mathcal{E}_1)$ be the set of the parts of this set. Figure 3.19 gives the lattice of $p(\mathcal{E}_1)$.

Let a subgraph of $\mathscr{L}_n^\sigma$ correspond to each part of $\mathcal{E}_1$ in the following way. The graph we want to balance being G_0, we associate graph G_i obtained from G_0 with the part u_i of $\mathcal{E}_i$ by changing the sign of the edges constituting u_i (Fig. 3.20); to the part $\emptyset$ corresponds G_0 itself, and to the part $\mathcal{E}_1$ corresponds the balanced graph we want to attain. It is clear that two graphs G_i and G_j corresponding to two parts u_i and u_j adjacent in the lattice of $p(\mathcal{E})$ are two adjacent graphs in $\mathscr{L}_n^\sigma$ and vice versa.

Therefore, the paths of the lattice of $p(\mathcal{E}_1)$ are paths of $\mathscr{L}_n^\sigma$, and it is on these paths that the balancing process takes place. But the lattice of $p(\mathcal{E}_1)$ is not a sublattice of $\mathscr{L}_n^\sigma$; indeed, if $u_i \subset u_j$, we would have in $\mathscr{L}_n^\sigma$, $G_i \subset G_j$ if and only if the edges changed into u_j and not into u_i were all changed from a negative to a positive sign; in fact, in $\mathscr{L}_n^\sigma$ the layout of the graphs in Fig. 3.20 is that represented by Fig. 3.21.

In Fig. 3.20, the *level* of a graph depends on the number of sign changes, and in Fig. 3.21, it depends on the number of positive edges. It is Fig. 3.20 that we must analyze in order to follow the balancing process; it is clear indeed that, *the more one climbs in this lattice*, the more *the unbalance degree is decreased*. The hypotheses are then translated in the following manner. A graph will be transformed into an *adjacent graph of higher level* in the lattices of the type of that in Fig. 3.20: from G_1, we will be able to pass to G_4 or G_5, but not to G_6, which is not adjacent, nor to G_2 or G_0, which are not of a higher level.

In order to make hypothesis H_4 more concrete, we must consider all the minimum balancing sets $\mathcal{E}_i$ and not only $\mathcal{E}_1$ as we have just done.

But let us stop for a moment: in order to study the passage from one algebraic graph to another, we have considered lattice $\mathscr{L}_n^\sigma$ of all the complete algebraic graphs of n points; then we consider the routes in $\mathscr{L}_n^\sigma$, that is, we consider $\mathscr{L}_n^\sigma$ as a graph (oriented): it is then a graph the points of which are graphs themselves. There is a change in the level of analysis here, which can confuse the reader. However, it will be necessary to proceed again with such changes of levels; for example, we will construct a graph each point of which will be a set of graphs. This is necessary, since these changes in levels are still the best means (whatever the difficulty for the untrained reader) to make certain properties of the previous level appear at a new level. In fact, the principle is the following: at a certain level of analysis, we face various structural proper-

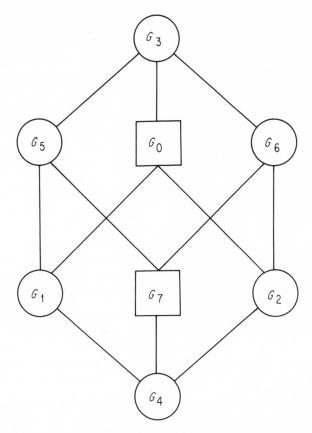

Figure 3.21

ties interwoven one into the other, but only one of which interests us; we then transform our plan of analysis by creating mathematical beings the structure of which is reduced to the property which interests us.

Let $\mathcal{E}_1, \mathcal{E}_2, \ldots, \mathcal{E}_r$ be the r minimum balancing sets $\mathcal{E}_i$ of a graph G, and $I = \{1, 2, \ldots, r\}$, the set of the *indices* of these sets. For each of these sets $\mathcal{E}_i$, we make the lattice of the parts $\mathfrak{p}(\mathcal{E}_i)$ as previously; then we *join* these r lattices into a single structure. The diagram very rapidly becomes impossible to represent so we will take a very much simplified example. Let $r = 3$, and $\mathcal{E}_1 = \{\alpha, \beta, \gamma\}, \mathcal{E}_2 = \{\beta, \gamma\ \delta\}$, and $\mathcal{E}_3 = \{\gamma, \delta, \varepsilon\}$, the Greek letters designating the *edges* of graph G. Figure 3.22 is obtained.

Let us designate by $u, u', \ldots$, the points of this union of lattices: they are the parts of the sets $\mathcal{E}_i$. Let $\mathfrak{p}$ be the set of these points u:

$$\mathfrak{p} = \bigcup_{i \in I} \mathfrak{p}(\mathcal{E}_i) = \{u, u', \ldots\}.$$

The union of a lattice can be considered as a graph L: $L = (\mathfrak{p}; \Gamma)$, with $(u, u') \in \Gamma$ if and only if $u \subset u'$ and $|u' - u| = 1$. In other words, L is the

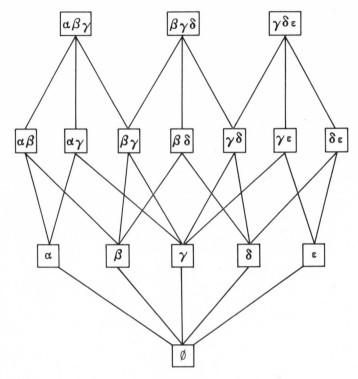

Figure 3.22

graph obtained from a diagram such as that of Fig. 3.22, by directing from the bottom to the top the lines which constitute it.

Hypothesis H_4 then becomes a random walk on L:

1. we start from $u = \emptyset$;

2. when we are at point $u \in p$ such that $|\Gamma u| \neq 0$, the probability of passing from u to $u' \in \Gamma u$ is equal to $1/|\Gamma u|$;

3. we stop upon reaching a point u such that $|\Gamma u| = 0$; this happens if and only if u is one of the sets $\mathcal{E}_i$ (since for any $i, j \in I$, we have $\mathcal{E}_i \not\subset \mathcal{E}_j$).

We then want to know what is the probability $p(\mathcal{E}_i)$ that an algebraic graph G_0 has of attaining the position of balance G_i, G_i being the graph obtained from G_0 by changing the sign of the edges appearing in $\mathcal{E}_i$.

Theoretically, this problem presents no difficulties: it can be entirely resolved on graph L, or on a *stochastic matrix* that we can associate with it (as will be seen later on). In practice, the computation quickly becomes embarrassingly large, and one wonders whether certain structural properties of graph L, related to its very particular construction, cannot permit a simplification of the computations, and at the same time, reveal certain mathematical properties which have remained unnoticed.

In order to undertake this study, we need a few theorems which will not be proven here, because they are nearly evident, and belong more to the theory of lattices than to that of graphs.

Let χ, χ', ... be any nonempty part of the set I of the indices distinguishing sets $\mathcal{E}_i$.

THEOREM 3.14.

$$\chi' \subset \chi \Leftrightarrow \bigcap_{i \in \chi} \mathcal{E}_i \subset \bigcap_{j \in \chi'} \mathcal{E}_j$$

THEOREM 3.15.

$$[u \in \bigcap_{i \in \chi} p(\mathcal{E}_i)] \Leftrightarrow [\text{ for any } \alpha \in u: \alpha \in \bigcap_{i \in \chi} \mathcal{E}_i].$$

THEOREM 3.16. *If* $\alpha \in u$,

$$\alpha \notin \bigcup_{i \in \chi} \mathcal{E}_i \Rightarrow u \notin \bigcup_{i \in \chi} p(\mathcal{E}_i).$$

THEOREM 3.17. *If* $u \subset u'$,

$$u \notin p(\mathcal{E}_i) \Rightarrow u' \notin p(\mathcal{E}_i).$$

These results admitted, we define, for any $\chi \subset I$,

$$Q_\chi = [\bigcap_{i \in \chi} p(\mathcal{E}_i)] - [\bigcup_{j \notin \chi} p(\mathcal{E}_j)].$$

THEOREM 3.18. *If Q is the set of the Q_χ, Q is a partition of* $p = \bigcup_{i \in I} p(\mathcal{E}_i)$, *that is,* $\bigcup_{\chi \subset I} Q_\chi = p$; *and for any χ and $\chi' \subset I$, $Q_\chi \cap Q_{\chi'} = \emptyset$.*

Proof. Let us show that $\bigcup_{\chi \subset I} Q_\chi = p$; that is, if $u \in p$ there exists a set of indices $\chi \subset I$ such that $u \in Q_\chi$; indeed, let χ be the set of indices $i \in I$ such that $u \in p(\mathcal{E}_i)$; we therefore have

$$u \in \bigcap_{i \in \chi} p(\mathcal{E}_i) \quad \text{and} \quad u \notin \bigcup_{j \notin \chi} p(\mathcal{E}_j);$$

hence $u \in Q_\chi$.

Let us show that for any χ and $\chi' \subset I$, we have $Q_\chi \cap Q_{\chi'} = \emptyset$. Suppose it is false. Let $u \in Q_\chi \cap Q_{\chi'}$ with $\chi \neq \chi'$; we have, for any $i \in \chi$,

$$u \in p(\mathcal{E}_i),$$

and for any $j \in \chi'$,

$$u \in p(\mathcal{E}_j).$$

If $\chi' - \chi \neq \emptyset$, let $h \in (\chi' - \chi)$; we have

$$h \notin \chi \quad \text{and} \quad u \in \bigcup_{h \notin \chi} p(\mathcal{E}_h);$$

hence $u \notin Q_\chi$.

If $\chi - \chi' \neq \emptyset$, we find $u \notin Q_{\chi'}$; there is therefore a contradiction in supposing $Q_\chi \cap Q_{\chi'} \neq \emptyset$.

We can make the definition of the Q_χ more concrete by considering the example in Fig. 3.22. Euler circles are utilized, representing the sets $p(\mathcal{E}_1)$, $p(\mathcal{E}_2)$, $p(\mathcal{E}_3)$, with $\mathcal{E}_1 = \{\alpha, \beta, \gamma\}$, $\mathcal{E}_2 = \{\beta, \gamma, \delta\}$, $\mathcal{E}_3 = \{\gamma, \delta, \varepsilon\}$ (Fig. 3.23). The intersections of the circles determine many *regions*, each of which corresponds to a set Q_χ:

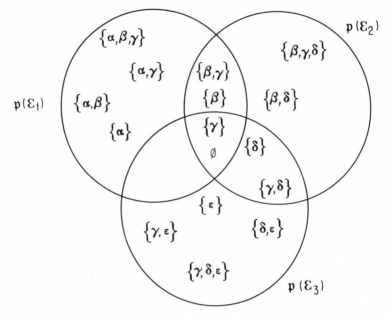

Figure 3.23

$$Q_{123} = \{ \emptyset, \{\gamma\} \}; \qquad Q_{23} = \{ \{\delta\}, \{\gamma, \delta\} \}; \qquad \text{etc.}$$

We notice that $Q_{13} = \emptyset$, that is, this set Q_{13} does not include any element of p—which is not to be confused with the presence in Q_{123} of $\{\emptyset\}$, element of p consisting in not changing any edge of algebraic graph G_0.

Associate with graph L a *reduced* graph L^0 (cf. Chap. 1, Sec. 5.4), defined by

$$L^0 = (Q; \Delta),$$

where Q is the set of the Q_χ and Δ: $(Q_\chi, Q_{\chi'}) \in \Delta$ if and only if $u \in Q_\chi$ and $u' \in Q_{\chi'}$ exist, such that $(u, u') \in \Gamma$.

THEOREM 3.19

$$(Q_\chi, Q_{\chi'}) \in \Delta \Rightarrow \chi' \subset \chi.$$

Proof. If $(Q_\chi, Q_{\chi'}) \in \Delta$, it is because $u \in Q_\chi$ and $u' \in Q_{\chi'}$ exist, such that $(u, u') \in \Gamma$, that is, such that $u \subset u'$; therefore, for any $\alpha \in u$, we have $\alpha \in u'$; but (Theorem 3.15), if $\alpha \in u$, then

$$\alpha \in \bigcap_{i \in \chi} \mathcal{E}_i;$$

hence,

$$\bigcap_{i \in \chi} \mathcal{E}_i \subset \bigcap_{i \in \chi'} \mathcal{E}_j \quad \text{and (Theorem 3.14)} \quad \chi' \subset \chi.$$

THEOREM 3.20. *If $u \in Q_\chi$, then $u' = u \cup \{\alpha\} \in Q_{\chi'}$, if and only if*

$$\alpha \in \left\{ \bigcap_{i \in \chi'} \mathcal{E}_i - \bigcup_{j \in \chi - \chi'} \mathcal{E}_j \right\}.$$

Proof of sufficiency. Let us show that $u' \in \bigcap_{i \in \chi'} p(\mathcal{E}_i)$. We have

$$u \in Q_\chi = u \in \bigcap_{h \in \chi} p(\mathcal{E}_h) \qquad \text{(definition of } Q_\chi\text{)}$$

$$\Rightarrow \text{for any } \beta \in u: \quad \beta \in \bigcap_{h \in \chi} \mathcal{E}_h \qquad \text{(Theorem 3.45)}.$$

On the other hand, we have the hypothesis: $u \subset u'$ and $|u' - u| = 1$; hence

$$(Q_\chi Q_{\chi'}) \in \Delta \qquad \text{(definition of } \Delta\text{)}$$

$$\Rightarrow \chi' \subset \chi \qquad \text{(Theorem 3.19)}$$

$$\Rightarrow \bigcap_{h \in \chi} \mathcal{E}_h \subset \bigcap_{i \in \chi'} \mathcal{E}_i \qquad \text{(Theorem 3.14)};$$

hence, for any $\beta \in u$, $\beta \in \bigcap_{i \in \chi'} \mathcal{E}_i$. Since

$$\alpha \in \{ \bigcap_{i \in \chi'} \mathcal{E}_i - \bigcup_{j \in \chi - \chi'} \mathcal{E}_j \},$$

we have $\alpha \in \bigcap_{i \in \chi'} \mathcal{E}_i$, and, for any $\beta \in u'$,

$$\beta \in \bigcap_{i \in \chi'} \mathcal{E}_i \Rightarrow u' \in \bigcap_{i \in \chi'} p(\mathcal{E}_i) \qquad \text{(Theorem 3.15)}.$$

Let us now show that $u' \notin \bigcup_{l \notin \chi'} p(\mathcal{E}_l)$. By definition of α,

$$\alpha \notin \bigcup_{j \in \chi - \chi'} \mathcal{E}_j,$$

hence $\qquad\qquad u' \notin \bigcup_{j \in \chi - \chi'} p(\mathcal{E}_j) \qquad \text{(Theorem 3.16)}.$

On the other hand,

$$u \in Q_\chi \Rightarrow u \notin \bigcup_{k \notin \chi} p(\mathcal{E}_k) \qquad \text{(definition of } Q_\chi\text{)}$$

$$\Rightarrow u' \notin \bigcup_{k \notin \chi} p(\mathcal{E}_k) \qquad \text{(Theorem 3.17)};$$

hence $\qquad\qquad u' \notin \bigcup_{l \notin \chi'} p(\mathcal{E}_l).$

We therefore see that $\qquad u' \in Q_{\chi'}.$

Proof of necessity. Let us show that if $u \in Q_\chi$ and $u' \in Q_{\chi'}$, with $u' - u = \{\alpha\}$, we have

$$\alpha \in \bigcap_{i \in \chi'} \mathcal{E}_i.$$

Indeed,

$$u' \in Q_{\chi'} \Rightarrow u' \in \bigcap_{i \in \chi'} p(\mathcal{E}_i) \qquad \text{(definition of } Q_{\chi'}\text{)}$$

and $\qquad\qquad \alpha \in u' \Rightarrow \alpha \in \bigcap_{i \in \chi'} \mathcal{E}_i \qquad \text{(Theorem 3.15)}.$

Let us show now that $\alpha \notin \bigcup_{j \in \chi - \chi'} \mathcal{E}_j$. Suppose that on the contrary

$$\alpha \in \bigcup_{j \in \chi - \chi'} \mathcal{E}_j;$$

for there exists a set of indices, $\chi'' \subset \chi - \chi', \chi'' \neq \emptyset$, such that

$$\alpha \in \bigcap_{h \in \chi''} \mathcal{E}_h.$$

Let $\chi''' = \chi' \cup \chi''$; we have then

$$\alpha \in \bigcap_{l \in \chi'''} \mathcal{E}_l \quad \text{and} \quad \alpha \notin \bigcup_{m \in \chi - \chi'''} \mathcal{E}_m;$$

hence, by the sufficient condition of the present theorem,

$$u' \in Q_{\chi'''} \neq Q_{\chi'};$$

which is contradictory; therefore

$$\alpha \notin \bigcup_{i \in \chi - \chi'} \mathcal{E}_j \quad \text{and} \quad \alpha \in \Big\{ \bigcap_{i \in \chi'} \mathcal{E}_i - \bigcup_{j \in \chi - \chi'} \mathcal{E}_j \Big\}.$$

This theorem is important, because it shows that an essential property of graphs L or L^0 can be expressed in function of the sets $\mathcal{E}_i$ without passing through the sets $p(\mathcal{E}_i)$; which considerably simplifies our problem.

THEOREM 3.21. *Whatever the point $u \in Q_\chi$ at which we happen to be, the probability (according to H_4) of going into $Q_{\chi'}$ is*

$$p(\chi\chi') = \frac{\Big| \bigcap_{i \in \chi'} \mathcal{E}_i - \bigcup_{j \in \chi - \chi'} \mathcal{E}_j \Big|}{\sum_{\chi''' \subset \chi} \Big| \bigcap_{h \in \chi''} \mathcal{E}_h - \bigcup_{l \in \chi - \chi''} \mathcal{E}_l \Big|}$$

Proof. Let u be a point of Q_χ; if

$$\alpha \in \Big\{ \bigcap_{i \in \chi'} \mathcal{E}_i - \bigcup_{j \in \chi - \chi'} \mathcal{E}_j \Big\},$$

by the preceding theorem, $u' = u \cup \{\alpha\}$ is a point of $Q_{\chi'}$, and since $u \subset u'$ and $|u' - u| = 1$, u' is adjacent to u in L. Therefore, in the balancing process, we will be able to go from u to u'; but in Q_χ, there are

$$\Big| \bigcap_{i \in \chi'} \mathcal{E}_i - \bigcup_{j \in \chi - \chi'} \mathcal{E}_j \Big|$$

adjacent points of u where we will be able to go from u; this result is independent of the particular u of Q_χ. Therefore, when we are in Q_χ, the probability of going into $Q_{\chi'}$ is proportional to

$$\Big| \bigcap_{i \in \chi'} \mathcal{E}_i - \bigcup_{j \in \chi - \chi'} \mathcal{E}_j \Big|;$$

in considering all the $Q_{\chi''}$ to which we can go from a point of Q_χ, that is, such that $\chi'' \subset \chi$ (Theorem 3.19), we find the formula of $p(\chi\chi')$ mentioned.

THEOREM 3.22. *The probability of a graph G becoming balanced according to the minimum balancing set $\mathcal{E}_i$ is*

$$p(\mathcal{E}_i) = \sum_{i \in \chi \subset I} \sum_{i \in \chi' \subset \chi} \cdots \sum_{i \in \chi''' \subset \chi''} p(I\chi) \cdot p(\chi\chi') \cdot \ldots \cdot p(\chi''\chi''') \cdot p(\chi'''i).$$

Proof. In order to prove this formula, it is convenient to associate with graph L^0 a *stochastic matrix* constructed in the following way.

Consider all the sets $\chi \subset I$; each of these sets is at the beginning and top of a row and a column of the matrix. If $\chi' \not\subset \chi$, zero is put into cell $(\chi\chi')$; if $\chi' \subset \chi$, $p(\chi\chi')$ is put into it. Zero is put into the diagonal cells if $|\chi| > 1$, and 1 is put there if $|\chi| = 1$. This matrix gives the probabilities of passing from Q_χ to $Q_{\chi'}$; it is clear that we go from Q_I to each Q_i in $(|I| - 1)$ stages (cf. Theorems 1.6 and 1.7). If, therefore, the matrix is raised to $(|I| - 1)$ power, we obtain in cell (Ii) the probability $p(\mathcal{E}_i)$, the theorem of which gives the formula.

Example. Let $\mathcal{E}_i = \{\alpha, \beta, \gamma\}$, $\mathcal{E}_2 = \{\beta, \gamma, \delta\}$, and $\mathcal{E}_3 = \{\gamma, \delta, \varepsilon\}$. We have sets Q_χ: $Q_{123}, Q_{12}, Q_{13}, Q_{23}, Q_1, Q_2, Q_3$.

First we construct a matrix giving to cell $(\chi\chi')$ the number

$$\left| \bigcap_{i\in\chi'} \mathcal{E}_i - \bigcup_{j\in\chi-\chi'} \mathcal{E}_j \right|$$

for χ' strictly included in χ:

	(123)	(12)	(13)	(23)	(1)	(2)	(3)	
(123)		1		1	1		1	4
(12)					1	1		2
(13)					2		2	4
(23)						1	1	2
(1)								
(2)								
(3)								

By dividing in each row by the total of the row, we obtain (Theorem 3.21) values $p(\chi\chi')$. We add the unit in cells $(1, 1)$, $(2, 2)$, and $(3, 3)$, and we have the following stochastic matrix:

	(123)	(12)	(13)	(23)	(1)	(2)	(3)	
(123)		.25		.25	.25		.25	1
(12)					.50	.50		1
(13)					.50		.50	1
(23)						.50	.50	1
(1)					1.			1
(2)						1.		1
(3)							1.	1

Since $|I| = 3$, we raise to power $(|I| - 1) = 2$. It is sufficient anyway to consider cells $[(123), (1)]$, $[(123), (2)]$, and $[(123), (3)]$. We find

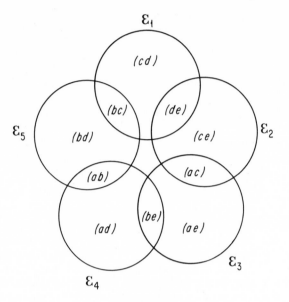

Figure 3.24

$$p(\mathcal{E}_1) = .375; \quad p(\mathcal{E}_2) = .250; \quad p(\mathcal{E}_3) = .375.$$

We verify that $\sum_i p(\mathcal{E}_i) = 1$.

We note that $p(\mathcal{E}_1) = p(\mathcal{E}_3)$; this comes from the symmetry of sets $\mathcal{E}_1$ and $\mathcal{E}_3$ in relation to set $\mathcal{E}_2$. Often such regulations in the relationships between sets $\mathcal{E}_i$ avoid the computations; thus, Fig. 3.24 gives the $r = 5$ minimum balancing sets of the graph in Fig. 3.13. This figure is sufficient to show that, in this case,

$$p(\mathcal{E}_i) = .20 \quad \text{for } i = 1, 2, \ldots, 5.$$

Other hypotheses on balancing processes. For hypotheses H_1 to H_4 we can substitute various hypotheses more or less similar. For example, we can re-work this set of hypotheses in order to integrate into it the following hypothesis:

(H_5) A graph tends at each stage to increase the number of its positive edges, to the degree compatible with the decrease in the unbalance degree.

This corresponds to the idea that the members of a group prefer maintaining friendly relations rather than hostile ones. Mathematically, it means that from one graph we pass to an adjacent graph, superior *at the same time* in L (cf., for example, Fig. 3.20) and in $\mathcal{L}_n^a$ (cf. Fig. 3.21). Therefore, to go from $G = (X; P, N)$ to $B_i = (X; P_i, N_i)$, a balanced graph obtained from the minimum balancing set $\mathcal{E}_i$ of G, we will necessarily pass by graph

$$G_i = (X; (P_i \cup P), (N_i \cap N);$$

we will therefore have to calculate, by the method previously shown, the probability of reaching each of these graphs G_i and then, from there, reaching graphs B_i. (Except for very particular cases, we will have a probability equal to one of reaching B_i if we happen to be in G_i.)

Many other hypotheses can be defined. In order to stay within the framework already explored, note that graphs $G' = (X; P', N')$ adjacent to a graph $G = (X; P, N)$ can be distributed into six classes, according to the following table:

$$\delta(G) - \delta(G')$$

		-1	0	$+1$
$|P| - |P'|$	-1	(11)	(12)	(13)
	$+1$	(21)	(22)	(23)

The hypotheses studied imply that we prefer (13) to (12) and (12) to (11) on the one hand, and on the other, (13) to (23), (12) to (22), (11) to (21); in fact, we always have (unless G is balanced) a representative of class (13) *or* of class (23).

If class (13) is empty, in H_5 we stated that (23) was preferred to the other classes; we could now state that (23) is preferred to (11), but that (12) is preferred to (23) . . ..

Other types of hypotheses: in a group, the balancing processes depend on the leader of the group, who first tries to balance the triangles in which he appears. It will then be sufficient to take this leader as the axis of the unbalance base of the graph, and the process will then be amenable to algebraic manipulation.

There is no reason to prefer one hypothesis to another: group psychology has as yet concerned itself too little with our problem, and the study of all possible hypotheses would come under mathematical games rather than under psycho-sociological research.

The examples we have studied or sketched lead now to the following work program. Whatever the proposed psychological hypotheses, they will formulate the dependence of the passage from a graph to another upon certain *relationships between the structures of the two graphs*. On the set of the possible graphs, we then define a *structure representing the relationships considered*, and this new program of analysis will permit the description of the consequences of the hypotheses kept.

We have previously (Theorem 3.22) utilized a stochastic matrix, that is, we have referred to the Markov processes. Some may think that the Markov techniques would have been sufficient, without graph theory. We would consult the matrix for the possible moves from one graph to the others; but this matrix will have some zero cells, others equal to one, and not arbitrarily; in fact, the structure of the matrix only represents the structural properties studied by graph theory. Besides, various works (Rouanet, 1960; Rosenblatt, 1957; see also Harary, 1959c) have shown that the study of Markov chains would gain from the theory of graphs; in particular, the asymptotic properties of a Markov chain immediately appeared on a graph which can be associated with the matrix defining the Markov chain. In the problem with which we are concerned, it is just this graph associated with the Markov chain which is directly determined by the structural study; and therefore the study of the problem can be made without any reference to the Markov processes.

6. Applications

Various *experimental studies* (Abelson and Rosenberg, 1958; Jordan, 1953; Morrisette, 1958) show that the theory of the balancing of graphs constitutes at least a good guide for the analysis of real psychological situations; however, these results do not greatly interest us here, because, on the one hand, the situations considered are represented by means of graphs more complex than the symmetric complete algebraic ones studied above, and, on the other hand, the authors have paid little attention to the very evolution of the processes.

Theorem 3.1, according to which a situation is in a state of balance only if the points can be distributed into two classes such that the intraclass relationships are positive and the interclass ones negative, is no doubt capable of an interesting *political application*. The politics of "blocs" at the world level could be mentioned, and the evolution of the votes at the U.N. could be studied from this viewpoint; but we should not forget that the search for balance as we have examined it is no doubt not the only factor in the evolution of group structures.

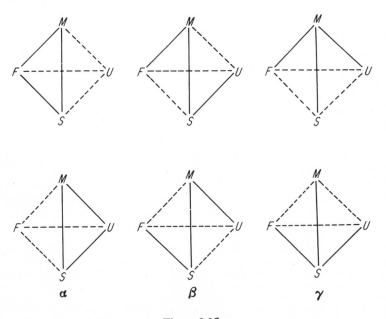

Figure 3.25

We will limit ourselves to the study of one anthropological application. Lévi-Strauss (1958, Chap. 2, pp. 50 ff.; Chap. 4, p. 38*) considers that the "kinship nucleus" in primitive societies is made up of the following four persons: the son (S), the father (F), the mother (M), and the maternal uncle (the mother's brother) (U). In each society studied, a great stability of the positive or negative relationships is observed between these four persons. The author gives only relations (FM), (MU), (US), (SF); according to the facts only six structures are observed. We tend to think that the two missing relationships (MS) and (UF) are, respectively, positive and negative, and this in all cases. We then get the six complete algebraic graphs of Fig. 3.25.

These six graphs are grouped into three classes, α, β, γ, of two graphs each, the two graphs of the same class being deduced one from the other by replacing F by U, and U by F, in α and β; and in γ, replacing M by S, and S by M.

Let us apply our analytic methods to these graphs. The following table is obtained.

	α	β	γ
δ	0	1	2
ε_i	$\emptyset$	$\{(MS)\}$	$\{(MS),\ (FU)\}$ $\{(MU),\ (FS)\}$ $\{(MF),\ (SU)\}$

First we notice that the graphs of the same class have exactly the same properties (from the point of view of our analysis).

Graphs α are in perfect balance.

Graphs β are moderately unbalanced, but the only minimum balancing set is made of edge (MS); it seems likely that this edge will resist a sign change, all the more so since the unbalance is weak. One can therefore expect various phenomena, although not clearly pronounced, that our model does not allow us to study in detail.

Finally, graphs γ are antibalanced (all triangles are negative). There are three minimum balancing sets, but one of them includes edge (MS) for which we have presumed a certain resistance to change. That leaves sets $\{(MU),$ $(FS)\}$ and $\{(MF), (SU)\}$. It is noticed that by utilizing one or the other of these two sets, each graph γ gives a graph α; we conclude that a family structure of type γ has little chance of survival, and that the disappearance of such

---

* C. Lévi-Strauss' book is a collection of articles. Chapter 2, "L'analyse structurale en linquistique et en anthropologie," has the footnote: "Publié sous ce titre, *Word, Journal of the Linguistic Circle of New York*, vol. 1, no. 2 (August 1945), pp. 1–21." Chapter 4, "Linguistique et anthropologie," has the footnote: "Traduit et adapté de l'original anglais, *Conference of Anthropologists and Linguists*, Bloomington, Indiana, 1952. Published on the basis of a transcription from a recording on a magnetic tape in *Supplement to International Journal of American Linguistics*, vol. 19, no. 2 (April 1953), mem. 8, 1953."

a structure leads to the appearance of a structure of type α.

But essentially on the basis of observation, and without any analysis referring to the theory of the balance of graphs, Lévi-Strauss (1958, p. 83) writes: "Arrangements of type α are often found; on the other hand, the arrangements of type β are frequent but often loose, and those of type γ are rare and perhaps impossible in a clear-cut form, since they would risk provoking a rupture of the elementary structure."

It seems that the agreement between the model and reality is fairly satisfactory.

Bibliography

Abelson, R. P., and M. J. Rosenberg, 1958, "Symbolic psycho-logic: a model of attitudinal cognition," *Behavior. Sc.*, **3**, 1–13.

Apostel, L., 1957, "Equilibre, logique et théorie des graphes," *in*: Apostel, Mandelbrot, and Piaget, *Logique et équilibre* (Paris, Presses Universitaires de France).

Bavelas, A., 1948, "A mathematical model for group structures," *Appl. Anthrop.*, **7**, 16–30.

Bavelas, A., 1950, "Communication patterns in task-oriented groups," *J. Acoust. Soc. Amer.*, **57**, 271–282.

Berge, C., 1958, *Théorie des graphes et ses applications* (Paris, Dunod).

Bratton, D., 1955, "Efficient communication networks," *Cowles Comm. Disc. Paper*, 2119.

Camion, P., 1960, "Quelques propriétés des chemins et circuits hamiltoniens dans la théorie des graphes," *Cahiers du Centre d'Etude et de Recherche Opérationnelle*, **2**: 1, 5–36.

Cartwright, D., and F. Harary, 1956, "Structural balance: a generalization of Heider's theory," *Psychol. Rev.*, **63**, 277–293.

Chandessais, C., 1957, "Application d'un modèle topologique à l'étude du moral," *Travail Humain*, **20**, 8–29.

Christie, L. S., R. D. Luce, and J. Macy, Jr., 1952, *Communication and learning in task-oriented groups*, Research Laboratory of Electronics, M.I.T., Technical Report 231.

Dailey, C. A., 1959, "Graph theory in the analysis of personal documents," *Hum. Relat.*, **12**, 65–74.

Deutsch, M., and H. B. Gerard, 1955, "A study of normative and informational social influences upon individual judgment," *J. Abn. Soc. Psychol.*, **51**, 629–636.

Egan, J. P., F. R. Clarke, and E. C. Carterette, 1956, "On the transmission and confirmation of messages in noise," *J. Acoust. Soc. Amer.*, **28**, 536–550.

Festinger, L., 1949, "The analysis of sociograms using matrix algebra," *Human. Rel.*, **2**, 153–158.

Festinger, L., 1950, "Informal social communication," *Psychol. Rev.*, **57**, 271–282.

Flament, C., 1956, "Changements de rôles et adaptation à la tâche dans des groupes de travail utilisant divers réseaux de communication," *Année Psychol.*, **56**, 411–432.

Flament, C., 1958a, "La performance des groupes de travail; rapports entre la structure de l'activité et celle du réseau de communication," *Année Psychol.*, **58**, 71–89.

Flament, C., 1958b, "L'étude mathématique des structures psycho-sociales," *Année Psychol.*, **58**, 119–131.

Flament, C., 1958c, "Performance et réseaux de communication," *Bulletin du Centre d'Etudes et de Recherches Psychotechniques*, **7**, 97–106.

Flament, C., 1958d, "Analyse pluridimensionnelle des structures hiérarchiques intransitives," *Bulletin du Centre d'Etudes et de Recherches Psychotechniques*, **7**, 171–179.

Flament, C., 1959a, "Nombre de cycles complets dans un réseau de communication; fonction caractéristique d'un graphe et ligne de Hamilton," *Bulletin du Centre d'Etudes et de Recherches Psychotechniques*, **8**, 105–110.

Flament, C., 1959b, "Modèle stratégique des processus d'influence sociale sur les jugements perceptifs," *Psychol. Française*, **4**, 91–101.

Flament, C., 1960, "L'étude structurale des groupes," *Bull. Psychol.*, **13**, 417–425.

Flament, C., 1961, "Processus d'influence sociale et réseau de communication," *Psychol. Française*, **6**, 115–125.

Flament, C., 1962a, "La mesure en psychologie sociale," *in:* Faverge, Flament, *et al.*, *Les problèmes de la mesure en psychologie* (Paris, Presses Universitaires de France).

Flament, C., 1962b, "Les processus de communication," *in:* Fraisse et Piaget, *Traité de psychologie expérimentale* (Paris, Presses Universitaires de France).

French, J. R. P., Jr., 1956, "A formal theory of social power," *Psychol. Rev.*, **63**, 181–194.

Frey, L., "La démocratie objectivement définie," *Rev. Française. Sc. Politique*, **10** 66–82.

Gilchrist, J. C., M. E. Shaw, and L. C. Walker, 1954, "Some effects of unequal distribution of information in a wheel group structure," *J. Abn. Soc. Psychol.*, **49**, 554–556.

Guetzkow, H, and H. A. Simon, 1955, "The impact of certain communication nets upon organization and performance in task-oriented groups," *Management Sc.*, **1**, 233–250.

Harary F., 1953, "On the notion of balance of a signed graph," *Mich. Math. J.*, **2**, 143–146.

Harary, F., 1955, "On local balance and *n*-balance in signed graphs," *Mich. Math. J.*, **3**, 37–41.

Harary, F., 1957, "Structural duality," *Behavior. Sc.*, **2**, 255–265.

Harary, F., 1959a, "Status and contra-status," *Sociometry*, **22**, 23–43.

Harary, F., 1959b, "On the measurement of structural balance," *Behavior, Sc.*, **4**, 316–323.

Harary, F., 1959c, "A criterion for unanimity in French's theory of social power, *in:* Cartwright, *Studies in social power* (Ann Arbor, Institute for Social Research).

Harary, F., and R. Z. Norman, 1953, *Graph theory as a mathematical model in social science* (Ann Arbor, Institute for Social Research).

Harary, F., and I. C. Ross, 1954, "The number of complete cycles in a communication network," *J. Soc. Psychol.*, **40**, 329–332.

Harary, F., and I. C. Ross, 1957, "A procedure for clique detection using the group matrix," *Sociometry*, **20**, 205–215.

Heider, F., 1946, "Attitudes and cognitive organization," *J. Psychol.*, **21**, 107–112.

Heise, G. A., and G. A. Miller, 1951, "Problem solving by small groups using various communication nets," *J. Abn. Soc. Psychol.*, **46**, 327–335.

Hirota, K., 1953, "Group problem solving and communication," *Jap. J. Psychol.*," **24**, 105–113.

Jordan, N., 1953, "Bahavioral forces that are a function of attitudes and of cognitive organization," *Hum. Relat.*, **6**, 273–287.

Kruskal, J. B. Jr., 1956, "On the shortest spanning subtree of a graph and the traveling salesman problem," *Proc. Amer. Math. Soc.*, **7**, 48–50.

Lanzetta, J. T., and T. B. Roby, 1955, *A framework for the study of work-group structure and task parameters*, USAF Personnel and Training Research Center, Randolph Field, Texas (unpublished draft).

Leavitt, H. J., 1951, "Some effects of certain patterns on group performance," *J. Abn. Soc. Psychol.*, **46**, 38–50.

Lévi-Strauss, C., 1958, *Anthropologie structurale* (Paris, Plon).

Lobstein, J., 1958, "Structure=réseau de communication," *Travail et Méthodes*, 67–73.

Luce, R. D., 1950, "Connectivity and generalized cliques in sociometric group structure," *Psychomet.*, **15**, 169–190.

Luce, R. D., 1951, *The theory of networks*, Group Network Laboratory, Research Laboratory of Electronics, M.I.T. (mimeographed).

Luce, R. D., 1952a, "A note on Boolean matrix theory," *Proc. Amer. Math. Soc.*, **3**, 382–388.

Luce, R. D., 1952b, "Two decomposition theorems for a class of finite oriented graphs," *Amer. J. Math.*, **74**, 701–722.

Luce, R. D., 1953, "Networks satisfying minimality conditions," *Amer. J. Math.*, **75**, 825–838.

Luce, R. D., J. Macy, Jr., L. S. Christie, and H. D. Hay, 1953, *Information flow in task-oriented groups*, Research Laboratory of Electronics, M.I.T., Technical Report 264.

Luce, R. D., and A. D. Perry, 1949, "A method of matrix analysis of group structure," *Psychomet.*, **14**, 95–116.

Macy, J., Jr., L. S. Christie, and R. D. Luce, 1953, "Coding noise in a task-oriented group," *J. Abn. Soc. Psychol.*, **48**, 401–409.

Mason, S. J., 1953, *On the logic of feedback*, Research Laboratory of Electronics, M.I.T., Technical Report 153.

Mason, S. J., 1956, "Feedback theory—further properties of signal-flow graphs," *Proc. Ire*, **44**, 920–926.

Miller, G. A., 1951, *Language and communication* (New York, McGraw-Hill Book Co.).

Morissette, J. O., 1958, "An experimental study of the theory of structural balance," *Hum. Rel.*, **11**, 329–354.

Mulder, M., 1959a, "Power and satisfaction in task-oriented groups," *Acta Psychol.*, **16**, 178–225.

Mulder, M., 1959b, "Group structure and group performance," *Acta. Psychol.*, **16**, 356–402.

Mulder, M., 1960a, "Communication structure, decision structure and group performance," *Sociometry*, **23**, 1–14.

Mulder, M., 1960b, "The power variable in communication experiments," *Hum. Rel.*, **13**, 241–257.

Restle, F., 1959, "A metric and an ordering on sets," *Psychometrika*, **24**, 207–220.

Restle, F., 1961, *Psychology of judgment and choice, a theoretical essay* (New York, John Wiley & Sons).

Roby, T. B., 1962, "Subtask phasing in small groups," *in*: Criswell, Solomon, and Suppes, *Mathematical Methods in Small Group Processes* (Stanford, Calif., Stanford University Press).

Rosenblatt, D., 1957, "On the graphs and asymptotic forms of finite Boolean relation matrices and stochastic matrices," *Naval Res. Logist. Quart.*, **4**, 151–168.

Ross, I. C., and F. Harary, 1952, "On the determination or redundancies in sociometric chains," *Psychomet.*, **17**, 195–208.

Ross, I. C., and F. Harary, 1955, "Identification of the liaison persons of an organization using the structure matrix," *Management Science*, **1**, 251–258.

Ross, I. C., and F. Harary, 1959, "A description of strengthening and weakening members of a group," *Sociometry*, **22**, 139–147.

Rouanet, H., 1960, "Les chaines de Markov en psychologie: introduction aux modèles stochastiques d'apprentissage," *Bull. Centre Etudes Recherches Psychotechniques*, **9**, 399–432.

Roy, B., 1961, *Cheminement et connexité dans les graphes: application aux problèmes d'ordonnancement* (Paris, Société d'Economie et de Mathematique Appliquée).

Shannon, C. E., 1948, "A mathematical theory of communication," *Bell System Tech. J.*, **27**, 380–423, 623–656.

Shaw, M. E., 1954a, "Group structure and the behavior of individuals in small groups," *J. Psychol.*, **38**, 139–149.

Shaw, M. E., 1954b, "Some effects of problem complexity upon problem solution efficiency in different communication nets," *J. Exper. Psychol.*, **48**, 211–217.

Shaw, M. E., 1954c, "Some effects of unequal distribution of information upon group performance in various communication nets," *J. Abn. Soc. Psychol.*, **49**, 547–553.

Shaw, M. E., 1955, "A comparison of two types of leadership in various communication nets," *J. Abn. Soc. Psychol.*, **50**, 127–134.

Shaw, M. E., 1956, "Random vs. systematic distribution of information in communication nets," *J. Personal.*, **25**, 59–69.

Shaw, M. E., and J. C. Gilchrist, 1956, "Intra-group communication and leader choice," *J. Soc. Psychol.*, **43**, 133–138.

Shaw, M. E. and G. H. Rothschild, 1956, "Some effects of prolonged experience in communication nets," *J. Appl. Psychol.*, **40**, 281–286.

Shaw, M. E., G. H. Rothschild, and J. F. Strickland, 1957, "Decision processes in communication nets," *J. Abn. Soc. Psychol.*, **54**, 323–330.

Shelly, M. W., and J. C. Gilchrist, 1958, "Some effects of communication requirements in group structures," *J. Soc. Psychol.*, **48**, 37–44.

Walker, L. C., *The effects of group size and group structure on problem-solving behavior in small groups* (unpublished manuscript).

———

Index

G

Graph, 52, 56, 72, 75; *see also* Arc, Point
adjacent, 110, 111, 122
algebraic, 46, 90, 118, 125
antibalanced, 98, 107
antibalanced complete algebraic, 106
application of theory of, 32
association of matrix with, 121
as tree, 66
automorphic, 52
balance, 95, 125
balance bases, 96
balance of complete algebraic, 93
balancing, 105
balancing algebraic, 108
calculating probability of reaching, 123
classification of, 98
communication network, 49
communications, 75
complete, 19
complete algebraic, 91, 95
completed symmetric, 40, 58
complete symmetric algebraic, 46
complex, 124
components, finding of, 35
connected, 66
connectivity in, 32–36, 50, 100
defined by correspondence, 18
definition of balance of, 91, 92
definition of simple, 44
degree of, 112
degree of balance, 98–107
deletion of arcs, 36
expression of essential property, 120
finding maximal strongly connected components, 34
generalized clique, 37
Hamiltonian paths in, 73
increase in positive edges, 122
lattice of n-points, 41
level, 114
m-balanced, 92
marked, 46, 60
measuring degree of unbalance, 99
μ-minimal, 58
μ-transitive closure, 58
n-point, 40, 97
nonoriented, 109
nonsymmetric, 24
number of balanced complete, 97

Graph (*Cont.*)
obtaining balanced, 102
partial, 22, 42
passage from, 114
paths, 17–25
probability of balance, 116
properties of balanced, 93
reduced, 118
reduction of, 22–23
reflexive, 19
relation to political theory, 124
relationship between structures, 123
representation, 20
representation of power relations, 87
representing network, 48
simple, 33
stability, 37
strengthening point in, 40
strongly connected, 34
symmetric, 19, 25, 36, 42, 44, 66
symmetric as clique, 37
symmetric connected, 33
table of base structure, 101
theory of balance of, 126
theory of balancing, 124
transformation into least unbalanced, 110
transitive, 19
transmission of information, 59
unbalanced, 90, 98
unbalanced algebraic, 108
unconnected, 38
uses of simple, 45
types of, 44–48
union and intersection on, 43
valuation of, 45
valued, 45, 74
Group, 45, 71
choice by, 54
communication network affecting, 47
completion of task by, 54
dependence on communication, 48
leader and balancing processes, 123
members, 44
normative attitude toward behavior of, 77
organization of, 78
power relations in, 87
preference for friendly relations, 122
structure, 107
unique point as constant, 72

Group, discussion, 53, 76
  experimental study of, 85, 86
Group, institutionalized, 47
Group, mixed, 46
Group, social, 21, 38; *see also* Sociogram
  communication needed for, 47
Group, work, 53
  choice of task models, 56
  efficiency, 82
  experimental study of, 77–78
  model preference of, 81
  optimal organization and, 76
  task, 48
  time for solution, 78
Group dynamics, 90

H

Harary, F., 73, 92, 93
Holders, initial, 71; *see also* Information, primary
Hypothesis, 107
  balancing algebraic graph, 108
  balancing processes, 122–23
  graph, transformation of, 110
  probability of passing from graph, 114

I

Idempotency, 57
Idempotent, 3; *see also* Power, Union
Image, 11; *see also* Function
Inclusion, 8, 14, 42; *see also* Relation
  strict, 10
Index, 50
  balance, 99
  decision centrality, 80
  significance, 51
  unbalance, 110
  validation of, 51n
Influence, social, 86, 87; *see also* Opinion
Information, 55; *see also* Communication
  alteration of, 75
  control, 75
  cost of relaying, 74
  definition of relays, 73, 74
  emission of, 63, 65
  exchange, 86
  final localization of, 54

Information (*Cont.*)
  intragroup communication, 52
  model of task, 58
  primary, 53, 55, 59, 78
  re-emission, 81
  requests for, 84, 85
  secondary, 55, 71
  transmission, 59, 71, 74
Information theory, 75
Internal semi-degree. *See* Reception, degree of
Intersection, 4
  empty, 3
Intransitivity, 100
Invariance, 57
Isomorphism, 40, 41, 52
  model-network, 82
Isotonicity, 57

K

Kernel, 37
  properties of, 38
Kruskal, J. B., 73
  case, 65, 66

L

Lattice, 15, 41, 75, 76, 108, 110
  climbing in, 114
  definition, 14
  graphic representation, 17
  n-point, 41, 42
  properties, 14
  theory of, 117
  union of, 115
Law, associative, 3
Law, commutative, 3, 6
Law, distributive, 4
Law, optimal pooling, 71
Leader, 123; *see also* Communication; Group, work
  choice of, 78
Length, 45; *see also* Path
  arborescence, 67
  of cycle, 99
  minimum, 59
  minimum total, 65

Numbers, prime, 2
Numbers, real, 45

O

Objects, 1
Operation, commutative, 5, 16
Operation, logical, 2
Operations, cost of, 56, 73
Opinion, 85; *see also* Communication, Information
influencing, 86
reduction of initial differences, 87
"or," as operation, 2
Order, 1
calculation of cost, 73
importance in pairs, 6
inclusion, 42
partial, 7
strict, 13
Order relation, 10, 12
Ordering, weak, 8
Organization, effective, 81, 82; *see also* Efficiency
Organization, optimal, 56–58, 60, 81
constraints, 75
definition of search, 59
search, 73
temporal, 74

P

Pairs, 5, 12, 18, 71
Partition, 7
definition, 9
Path, 17–25, 34, 58, 66, 110, 111; *see also* Chain, Track
direct communication, 49
elementary, 23, 29
Hamiltonian, 24
in valued graph, 45
length, 25, 45
shortest, 74
Paths, 31, 59, 114
divergent, 24
elementary, 32
Hamiltonian, 73
length, 29

Paths (*Cont.*)
methods for finding, 32
transmission, 74
types, 32
Peers, 21
Performance, deterioration of, 74
Phenomena, 22
Point, 31, 34, 60, 62, 67, 70, 91, 120; *see also* Communication, Graph, Track
arbitrary, 34, 93, 95
articulation, 38, 39, 83
computing deviations from, 26
connectivity and, 32–36
consecutive on order, 73
corresponding, 68
graph as, 114
optimal pooling, 72
pooling, 71, 79, 83
psychological reasons for saturation, 74
terminal, 29, 81
unique, 63, 66, 79
unique as constant, 72
Points, 18, 59
correspondence between, 41
disparity among, 52
power, 38, 40
practice, 38
for relay, 49
removal of, 40
Pooling, 55; *see also* Information
localization, 54
optimal, 71, 72
Popularity, 21
Position, privileged, 39
Possibilities, local, 110
Power, 2
as distance, 15, 16
square matrix, 28
Problems, solving, 78
Process, balancing, 89–126
Processes, influence, 88
Product, 6
associative, 95
Cartesian, 5, 6, 12, 100
Proof, 119
Properties, 114; *see also* Antisymmetry, Reflexivity, Symmetry, Transitivity
structural, 115
unnoticed mathematical, 117
Property, as definition of set, 2
Psychology, 44